MAN AND THE HEAVENS

On March 13, 1956, the first man-made starlight appeared in the skies over New Mexico. This milestone marked the distance man has traveled from his primitive ancestors who worshiped the austere bodies of the heavens as their gods.

Here is a delightful recounting of the results of man's insatiable quest for knowledge and how discovery of his origins came from clues in the air above him.

The atmosphere is the mother of life on earth, and its protecting wing shields us from the ravages of outer space. It is also the source of phenomena that have awed or terrified man throughout his history —sunsets, rainbows, mirages, tornadoes, tidal waves.

The author discusses all these phenomena and dispels much of the mystery, but none of the wonder. He speculates on the atmospheres of other planets and the possibilities of life on them, considers the threat of radioactive dust to earth, and looks to the future, when man will perhaps control the path of wind, storm, and weather, through his greater knowledge of earth's life-giving canopy.

Other MENTOR Books You'll Enjoy

The Crust of the Earth *Edited by Samuel Rapport and Helen Wright*

Selections from the writings of the best geologists of today, telling the fascinating story of billions of years in the life of the earth. (#MD264—50¢)

The Universe and Doctor Einstein (revised)
by Lincoln Barnett

A clear analysis of time-space-motion concepts and the structure of atoms. Foreword by Albert Einstein. (#MD231—50¢)

Biography of the Earth (revised) *by George Gamow*

A simply written and authoritative life story of the planet Earth, its past, present and future profusely illustrated. (#MD138—50¢)

The Birth and Death of the Sun (revised)
by George Gamow

Stellar evolution and the anatomy of matter as modern physics has explored it. Illustrated. (#MD120—50¢)

THEO LOEBSACK

Our Atmosphere

TRANSLATED FROM THE GERMAN
BY E. L. AND D. REWALD

A MENTOR BOOK

Published by THE NEW AMERICAN LIBRARY

Published as a MENTOR BOOK
By Arrangement with Pantheon Books, Inc.

First Printing, January, 1961

MENTOR BOOKS are published by
The New American Library of World Literature, Inc.
501 Madison Avenue, New York 22, New York

PRINTED IN THE UNITED STATES OF AMERICA

To My Wife

PART THREE

MAN AND THE AIR

LIST OF PLATES

(*between pages 96-97*)

PREFACE

IN 1953 the American chemist Stanley Miller made an astonishing discovery. He found indications that the air enveloping the earth played an important role in the creation of life, two or three thousand million years ago. Miller succeeded in producing a blend of gases which resembled the primordial atmosphere of our planet. Under the influence of electric sparks there appeared in this blend of gases some chemical compounds which are basic to living matter. To-day the air has a different composition, and life can only come from matter that is already living, but although the air has changed it is still essential for life.

The air is an invisible element which we usually consider only in connection with weather, flying and breathing, but since Miller's experiment it can claim equal rank with the seas as a forefather of life. The air, like the sea, is a storehouse of innumerable mysterious and curious things. The strange play of sunlight on water droplets in the atmosphere, the phenomenon of sound, mirages, the well-being of mankind and the danger of radio-active dust are only a few of them.

This book deals with these and other subjects. It tells of the wonders and riddles of the air, not just of their history and discovery but, even more, of their function and influence. I have tried to keep the language descriptive and clear. This has its drawbacks. The understanding of modern scientific thought and problems requires the specialised knowledge of an expert. The greater the conquest of new fields by modern research the harder it becomes to make the results generally comprehensible. Take for example, the problems of nuclear physics and their vital importance to mankind. Clarity and logic are no longer sufficient to expound the forces involved in the decomposition and change in an atomic nucleus.

In an attempt to give easily understood explanations to laymen, the author is in constant danger of either creating incorrect concepts or escaping into technical language, with a consequent loss of clarity. These are the difficulties and they represent the limits of all books of popular science. Nevertheless, the stretching of these limits to their maximum has an irresistible fascination for those who have tried it.

It is my hope that this book has something to offer to the expert as well as to the layman. Without pretending to be complete it may give a picture of the atmosphere, earth's envelope, which is constantly around and inside us, but about which we really know so little. It may contribute to our knowledge of the air, and I believe that the air will give us much concern in the years to come. Since the first atomic bomb was exploded, the air has been filled with billions of minute radioactive dust particles. This radio-active dust has already become a major problem of our world and we must take it very, very seriously, for it is possible that the atmosphere which once helped to create life could with its sinister freight threaten its very existence.

In this book I have dealt with the problems of many branches of science and my personal knowledge would not have been sufficient to ensure accuracy on all points. I have, therefore, asked a number of specialists to help me, and they have kindly lent me their aid. I would like to express my gratitude to the following for expert advice and for checking individual chapters:

Professor S. Baumbach; Dr. E. Fromm; Professor K. Heyns; Dr. Korp, Dipl. Ing.; Dr. F. Krügler; Dr. O. Moese; Dr. E. Schücking; Dr. W. Walter (all of Hamburg); Dr. C. Labs, of Heidelberg; and Dr. H. Langendorff of Freiburg.

THEO LOEBSACK

PART ONE

THE AIR AROUND US

1

THE HISTORY OF THE ATMOSPHERE

THIS BOOK DEALS WITH A SUBSTANCE that is invisible, tasteless, formless and colourless. Yet it is more intimately connected with our lives than anything else in the world. It is the air that always and everywhere surrounds us wherever we are. It is an essential part of our lives from the moment of our birth, even more important than sunlight and food, for without it we would die in a few minutes.

Most of us take the air for granted, or believe it to be immutable from now to eternity; but this is an error, for the atmosphere, just like the land and sea which make up the rest of our world, has a long history behind it and is still changing. It was the unique composition of the primordial atmosphere two or three thousand million years ago that helped to create the first living matter. It is the oxygen-containing air of to-day that sustains life and, in the distant future, by an alteration of quantity may end it.

If we want to unravel the secrets of the origin of our atmosphere we must also investigate the creation of the earth, for the birth and subsequent development of both are inextricably linked.

The most modern way of "dating" geological formations by radio-activity shows the earth to be four or five thousand million years old. The investigation of light from distant nebulæ shows that the universe is expanding rapidly. If one calculates backwards from the rate of this expansion (like running a film backwards through a cinema projector), one reaches a point at which the universe must have been created by the explosion of an extraordinarily dense clump of matter. This primeval explosion also took place about four or five thousand million years ago. Our planet was probably created at the same time and has been going its own way ever since.

In its earliest youth the earth was extremely hot. It had no air around it, as we understand that word, but was en-

veloped by a thick mass of hot gases. This stinking, poisonous mixture could not have supported life (even if the temperature had been lower), for it probably contained ammonia
and the hydrogen compounds of fluorine, chlorine, bromine
and sulphur. The temperature was possibly several thousand
degrees centigrade, and this had the advantage that it gave
such speed to most of the gas molecules that they could
escape from the gravitational field of the earth into outer
space.

As the earth grew colder and colder its crust gradually
solidified and the air slowly filled with gases which had been
dissolved in the liquid rock, such as water vapour, nitrogen
and carbon dioxide.[1] This can be called the second phase of
the primordial atmosphere. We can obtain a faint idea of its
composition by comparing it to the emanation of modern
volcanoes. The Halemaumau volcano on Hawaii, for instance,
throws out clouds containing 68 per cent water vapour, 13
per cent carbon dioxide and 8 per cent nitrogen, the rest
being made up of sulphurous fumes.

This second phase could still not support life as it was
highly poisonous. The thick, dank, viscous clouds may have
presented a picture similar to that described in the Bible:

> And the earth was without form and void; and darkness
> was upon the face of the deep.

or the Edda:

> There was neither sand nor sea nor waves, not earth be-
> low nor sky above; yawning abyss, and nowhere green.

At one time during the gradual cooling process, the air
temperature must have fallen to a point where water vapour
and liquid water could exist side by side. Scientists call this
the "critical temperature" and it lies at 374.2 degrees centigrade. Soon after this, the first droplets of water appeared
in the atmosphere and a most peculiar thing happened. It
began to rain, but it rained only in the sky. As the rain fell
and neared the hot crust the raindrops evaporated. The hot
water vapour rose, cooled, condensed into raindrops, and the
cycle began all over again. Only when the crust itself had
cooled sufficiently could the raindrops fall on to the land to
form the rivers, lakes and oceans which began to erode the
continents.

At this time a large amount of the atmospheric carbon
dioxide disappeared, some of it in the weathering of feldspar,

---

[1] According to the Russian scientist Oparin, the hydrocarbons were
created by contact between water vapour in the atmosphere and
metallic carbides in the crust of the earth.

some of it in the formation of limestone and some of it by dissolving in the oceans. (There is to-day three hundred thousand times more carbon dioxide bound up in limestone and dolomitic rock than free in the atmosphere.)

The Russian scientist Oparin and his American colleague Urey believe that the primeval atmosphere of two or three thousand million years ago already contained the components which made the development of life in later ages possible. According to their hypothesis, these consisted of simple hydrocarbons such as methane (marsh gas), ammonia, hydrogen and water vapour. This may be called the third phase in the history of the atmosphere. The thick, dark layer of clouds began to show cracks through which the sunlight could fall onto the hot oceans for the first time. No plants or animals existed, but thunderstorms raged across the surface, volcanoes exploded and from the earth's centre mighty forces squeezed and folded the crust into mountains and continents. Torrential rains began to erode the mountains, and streams and rivers carried the stones and rubble into the seas, where it was deposited in thick layers.

It was during this dark and tempestuous stage that the material foundations of life were laid. At some time during this phase the first organic substances, the bricks of life, were created. But where? And when?

It is unlikely that the first question will ever be answered, but we have several informative hints about the hotly contested "how." At the beginning of this century the German chemist Löb began to think about the origin of organic matter. He was the first to realise, in 1912, that in contrast to our present oxygen-containing air, the atmosphere in the far past must at one time have been a "reducing" one. In its chemical sense this word means that free oxygen is consumed and converted into oxygen-containing substances. In 1953 the American chemist Stanley Miller carried out some important experiments. He proceeded from the hypotheses that his teacher, Urey, and Oparin had advanced about the primordial atmosphere. Believing that there must have been lightning—just as in thunderstorms to-day—which was strong and frequent, he tried to reconstruct the atmospheric conditions of two to three thousand million years ago. Taking a blend of certain proportions of methane, ammonia and hydrogen he introduced it into an evacuated glass sphere. This sphere was connected to another glass vessel containing boiling water. The water vapour mingled with the other gases and the mixture was then passed over a constantly sparking electric arc.

Then something remarkable happened, something that was

thought impossible. After circulating for eight days over the artificial lightning, Miller's "primordial atmosphere" was found to have given rise to a few milligrams of organic substances. The most extraordinary thing was that some of these substances belonged to that group of compounds from which living matter is built up—the so-called amino-acids—such as glycine and α and β-alanine. Under strictly scientific conditions it had been shown that the very fundamentals of living matter could be made from inorganic substances. Similar investigations by Professor Heyns and his colleagues in Hamburg confirmed and extended Miller's results showing, for instance, the formation of guanidine compounds, presumably the precursors of the biologically important nucleic acids.

Of course, these amino-acids cannot be called alive, just as one would not call a single brick a house or a village, nor do the experiments show how these small units were synthesised into complex proteins and finally made into living cells. The steps up the evolutionary ladder from inanimate material to living matter have not yet been satisfactorily explained; we can only guess how nature went to work. There is a strong probability that, about 2500 million years ago, the air contained a random collection of organic substances which had been formed by the action of heat and lightning on the gases of the atmosphere. All kinds of reactions must have taken place between these compounds, and many of them were probably leached into the oceans by raindrops. Dissolved in the warm seas they were protected from the

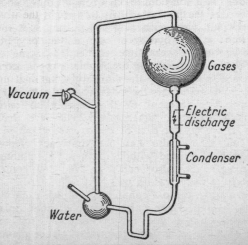

Stanley L. Miller's experiment.

decomposing action of the oxygen which appeared in the atmosphere at a later period. Some of these dissolved compounds may have gradually combined into more complex structures, similar to those found in living matter to-day. The one thing that did not matter was time; a million years more or less were of no account, until sometime, somewhere in the sea a small lump of protein was produced which possessed one or more of the characteristics of life: digestion, reproduction, response to stimulus. . . .

Recent biochemical research has given us some insight into this puzzle of creation. It has been found that certain groups of atoms concerned in the synthesis of proteins will preferentially combine with each other under specific conditions. This makes it likely that coincidence plays a much smaller role in the creation of the precursors of living matter than has been previously supposed. We also know that there would be no life now if the atmosphere of three or four thousand million years ago had not had its unique composition, or if it had contained oxygen.

The oxygen in the atmosphere has a very unusual history. It appeared at a fairly late stage, long after the other gases such as nitrogen, carbon dioxide and water vapour. It is unique among the components of the atmosphere, and scientists needed all their ingenuity to unravel its origin. We now believe that it was liberated by two independent processes. According to Harteck's theory it was formed in the highest layers of the atmosphere in the following way. Some water vapour rose (as it still does to-day) to a height of about forty miles above the earth's surface. At this height the ultra-violet rays of the sun have such power that they split the water vapour into atomic hydrogen and atomic oxygen. Since hydrogen atoms are very light and mobile some of them escaped into outer space, but the heavier oxygen atoms were kept in the atmosphere by the earth's gravitational pull. The debatable point about this theory is whether sufficient oxygen could have been created in this manner to enrich the primordial atmosphere. Other scientists believe that plants gave rise to the greater part of the oxygen found in the air to-day. This theory also has one drawback. How could plants ever have existed without oxygen for, although they give off oxygen, they also need it to live. How could plants have evolved if there was no free oxygen on earth?

This seems like the old conundrum: which came first, the chicken or the egg? There is, however, a possible explanation, namely that oxygen was not as essential for the first primitive plants as it is for present-day higher plants. That some plants can live without oxygen is proved by certain

Cross-section showing the most important properties of our atmosphere, up to a height of 240 miles.

Air temperatures (second scale from the right) above 120 miles depend on the thermal variations of the electrically charged air molecules. (This drawing is based on the German original; 1 kilometre equals ⅝ mile.)

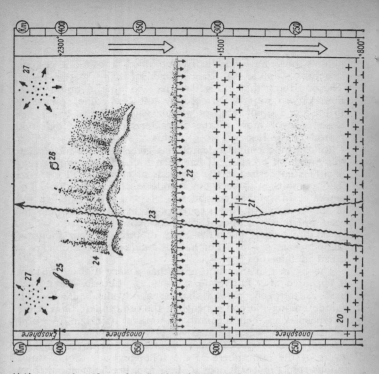

27. In the exosphere (above 250 miles) the air consists of only a few, freely moving particles. Some of these escape into outer space because the gravitational pull of the earth is not strong enough to hold them; others sink back into the lower layers.

26. Artificial satellites circle the earth in an elliptical orbit several hundred miles above the surface.

25. The American rocket WAC Corporal reached a height of about 250 miles in 1949.

24. The upper fringe of the polar lights curtain is usually between 125 and 600 miles above the earth's surface.

23. Ultra short (television) waves are not reflected by any of the electrically charged layers. If directed upwards they escape into space.

22. Cosmic dust: between 1000 and 2000 tons fall on earth daily. This increase in weight is probably compensated by the escape of air particles into space.

21. Zone of electrically charged air (F_2 layer), which reflects radio short waves back to earth.

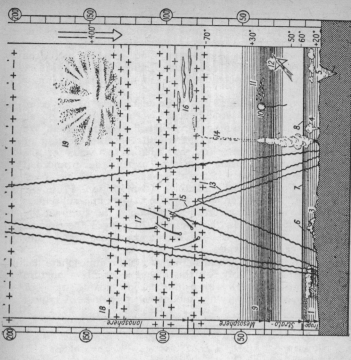
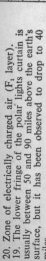
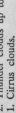

20. Zone of electrically charged air (F₁ layer).

19. The lower fringe of the polar lights curtain is usually between 50 and 90 miles above the earth's surface, but it has been observed to drop to 40 miles.

18. Zone of electrically charged air (E₂ layer).

17. Meteors meet sufficient air resistance to burn away by friction, causing shooting stars.

16. Noctilucent clouds.

15. Zone of electrically charged air (E₁ layer), which reflects radio short waves back to earth.

14. Ash from the eruption of Krakatoa thrown to a height of 50 miles.

13. Zone of electrically charged air (D layer), which reflects radio long waves back to earth.

12. Rocket powered aeroplane reaches a height of about 18 miles.

11. Iridescent or mother of pearl clouds, up to 25 miles.

10. Weather balloons reach a height of 25 miles.

9. Ozone layer.

8. Jet-stream currents of high velocity.

7. Sky colour becomes black, stars visible in daytime.

6. Sky colour dark violet.

5. Greatest known depth of ocean (35,958 feet).

4. Atomic explosion "mushroom" reaches a height of about 6 miles.

3. Mount Everest, highest peak on earth, 29,028 feet.

2. Thunder clouds up to 6 miles.

1. Cirrus clouds.

types of sulphur bacteria, and it is possible that the first primitive living cells resembled them in liberating oxygen without consuming it themselves. Once oxygen had been produced the primitive cells could climb the evolutionary scale, creating increasingly higher and more complex forms terminating in man.

All this does not touch the ultimate mystery of life or of being. This mystery is connected with the origin of all matter and it seems unlikely that it will ever be solved. We can say, however, that the prerequisites of the creation of life occurred only once in the millions of years of the earth's existence, during the time when the primordial atmosphere enveloped it. Since that phase the earth has never again had that essential and unique composition. From the stage when free oxygen first appeared, inorganic substances could no longer be converted to organic matter without the aid of living things. In the presence of oxygen the organic compounds would have been decomposed into water, ammonia and carbon dioxide.

For the last two thousand million years the atmosphere has not changed appreciably. To this day it is mainly a mixture of nitrogen and oxygen with a little carbon dioxide, traces of rare inert gases and varying amounts of impurities. A typical analysis is:

Constant components

Nitrogen	N_2	78.084%	by volume	
Oxygen	O_2	20.946%	"	"
Argon	A	0.934%	"	"
Carbon dioxide	CO_2	0.033%	"	"
Neon	Ne	0.00001818%	"	"
Helium	He	0.00000524%	"	"
Methane	CH_4	0.000002%	"	"
Krypton	Kr	0.00000114%	"	"
Hydrogen	H_2	0.0000005%	"	"
Nitrous Oxide	N_2O	0.0000005%	"	"
Xenon	Xe	0.000000087%	"	"

Variable components

Water vapour	H_2O
Ozone	O_3
Hydrogen peroxide	H_2O_2
Ammonia	NH_3
Sulphuretted hydrogen	H_2S
Sulphur dioxide	SO_2
Sulphur trioxide	SO_3
Carbon monoxide	CO
Radon	R
Dust, soot, salt particles	

Over millions of years the air has retained its delicate and beneficial balance of components. Does it not seem dangerous, therefore, that during the last hundred years man has begun to poison it continuously? Factory chimneys, exhaust pipes and atomic explosions have raised the grim spectre of atmospheric pollution. These impurities do not yet threaten our lives, but we should be on our guard. Our very existence is imperilled and we should not take this threat too lightheartedly.

2

THE LAYERS OF THE ATMOSPHERE

WHAT CHILD HAS NOT HAD THE PAINFUL EXPERIENCE of seeing a treasured balloon sail away into the distance? I well remember a brilliant red balloon which kept me completely happy for a whole afternoon, until, while I was playing, a clumsy movement allowed it to escape. Spellbound, I gazed after it as it drifted silently away, gently swaying, growing smaller and smaller, until it was only a tiny red point in a blue sky. At that moment I realised, for the first time, the vastness above us; a huge space without visible limits. It was an apparent void, full of secrets, exerting an inexplicable power over all the earth's inhabitants. I believe that many people, consciously or unconsciously, have been filled with awe by the immensity of the atmosphere. All our knowledge about the air, gathered over hundreds of years, has not diminished this feeling.

More than two-thirds of the earth's crust is covered by water, but all these oceans combined are only a small puddle compared to the measureless sea of air which fills the sky above us. It surrounds the earth like a gigantic husk, to a height of several hundred miles. It reaches into all valleys and hollows and fills every man-made depression. It penetrates into the finest rock crevices, between the petals of a flower and between the pages of this book. It covers every inch of the 197 million square miles of the earth's surface and, if we calculate how much force it exerts on our planet, we have to write a five with fifteen noughts behind it to give the weight in tons. This is equal to the weight of about 33,000 million large railway engines and their tenders. If these engines were coupled together they would circle the world two and a half million times. About 95 per cent of this huge mass of air is concentrated in a layer up to twelve miles above the earth's crust; the remaining 5 per cent is dispersed above it to a height of several hundred miles.

This sea of gases is not dead. It is as full of life as a cultivated garden. In the densest bottom layer live an incalculable number of plants, more than a million species of animal and about 2700 million human beings. It is a teeming mass of growing, flowering, and breathing individuals, and no one can tell how long these will be able to go on multiplying before they run short of air. These are only the inhabitants of the earth's crust, who, like the deep-sea fishes, have adapted themselves to the enormous pressure of their environment; there is also an abundance of life above them. Up to a height of about six miles the air is full of suspended bacteria, fungal spores and pollen grains. During a balloon ascent in 1936 the scientist Perlewitz found that, between 2500 and 4500 feet, a cube of air the size of a lump of sugar contained from 19 to 120 germs, among them mould-spores, cocci and yeast species.

The air is also full of inanimate matter such as dust, soot, volcanic ash, salt crystals from sea spray, and fine sand grains raised by storms in the deserts. In addition to these there is cosmic star dust. Each day a weight of two to three thousand tons of this dust falls out of the universe on to the earth. This huge mass would increase the weight of our planet appreciably if tiny particles of the atmosphere did not simultaneously wander off into space.

Although the air at sea-level is made up of the same constituents as at great heights, it becomes less dense as we go higher. At about six miles it is already so thin that a man would suffocate if he stayed in it for more than a few minutes. At twelve miles you could not light a candle because there is not enough oxygen to keep it burning. In the thin air of great heights the number of gas molecules per cubic inch is very small. In other words, the distance between the air particles grows with increasing height. Thus, for every ten million million air molecules at sea-level, there are only one thousand at six hundred miles, and only one molecule at nine hundred miles.

One can no more define the upper limit of the atmosphere than the outline of a puff of smoke. Somewhere, far above the earth, the air gradually merges into infinite space, and we only know that this "somewhere" lies at a height of between two hundred and sixty and nine hundred miles.

Although the air above us appears uniform, the scientists have found that the atmosphere is divided into distinct storeys. Just as the earth is composed of geological strata, the air has different layers, each one with its own characteristics.

Let us imagine a powerful lift capable of rising at 60 miles per hour through these storeys to the upper limit of the atmosphere. The pressurised cabin of this lift would have a circular observation window and a thermometer protected against the direct rays of the sun, as well as an altimeter and an instrument for measuring electric charges. We enter the cabin, the altimeter reads zero, the thermometer shows 20° C. . . . the engine starts and we begin to rise. After only five to eight minutes we have climbed through the first storey; this is the troposphere (from the Greek *tropos*: turning). In this layer occur the meteorological changes, when cold, dry air masses meet damper and warmer ones. This is the turbulent region where clouds and rainbows are formed, as well as gales, monsoons and sandstorms, where cloudbursts, hail, thunder and lightning rage.

As a rule the temperature gets colder as we rise higher in this zone and at the upper limit it falls to –60° C. On earth such low temperatures only occur during severe winters in Siberia. The temperature at this upper edge varies according to our starting point. If we start in the polar regions it would be about –50° C., but if we begin in the tropics the thermometer might fall to –80° C.

We must remember that the earth is not a perfect sphere. It not only has a very rough surface but is slightly flattened, as if giant hands had squeezed it gently at the poles; the geophysicists call it an "ellipsoid of revolution." In the course of millions of years the gyration of the earth and the consequently greater centrifugal power at the equator have caused an extrusion in this region. Oddly enough the troposphere is also influenced by this centrifugal force; in other words it is not uniformly distributed about the earth but its mass bellies out around the equator. Here the troposphere has a depth of about eleven miles, whereas it measures only five miles at the poles.

The altimeter rises. If we had started in the foothills of the Himalayas we would at this moment be passing the tip of Mount Everest. We are more than five and a half miles above the earth. What surrounds us? A cloudless, deep blue sky, with an intensity of colour never seen from the surface of the earth. This raises the question: "Why is the sky up here so deep a blue, and why does it appear blue to people on earth rather than yellow, green, pink or red?"

The answer lies in the nature of sunlight, which is composed of the colours of the rainbow. If we pass a ray of sunlight through a glass prism it is broken up in a curious way, and as a result we see a fan of colours: violet, blue, green, yellow and red. If we examine this fan closely we observe that the violet rays are deflected farthest from the direction of the original white sunbeam. This explains the blueness of the sky, for the air particles deflect the rays of sunlight. Their scattering power is greatest on the violet and blue rays, much less on the yellow and almost non-existent on the red. Once the blue rays are deflected they meet other air particles which deflect them again, and this is repeated endlessly, causing them to follow a zigzag course through the air. When they finally reach us, they do not seem to come directly from the sun but, like a fine spray of rain, from all corners of the sky. Thus the sky appears blue and the sun yellow, because the yellow and red rays undergo less scattering and reach us in a direct line. In the evening, when the sunrays have to traverse an exceptionally thick layer of air, even the yellow light is filtered out by the atmosphere and only the red rays of longer wavelength reach us in an almost straight line, producing the deep red of the evening sun.

"All right," you may say, "but how do you explain why the sky grows darker with increasing height?" It is very simple. At great heights the sunrays meet far fewer air particles than at sea-level and are scattered and deflected less frequently. Therefore the light no longer seems to come from all around us, but to be concentrated mainly at its source: the sun. Where there is no light there can be no coloured sky. Because of this the sky at great heights is black as night, and the sun shines with a dazzling white intensity.

In the meantime, the thermometer outside our window has remained at its low level. Merciless cold meets us as we enter the next storey. It is the stratosphere (from the Latin *stratum*: layer), the vestibule to outer space. The air in the stratosphere is dry, transparent and extremely thin. No snow flakes or rain drops touch our cabin and no clouds pass us. The air is clearer than rock crystal and surrounds us like a huge vacuum chamber. If we opened our door, or if a meteor shattered our window, the air would hiss out as if from an exploded football. In these circumstances we would not live longer than a few minutes, for, as a result of the low air pressure around us, the blood would bubble in our veins. Before this horrid fate overtook us, we might just have enough time to remember our physics lessons, which told us that the boiling point of a liquid is lowered by a decrease in pressure. At about fourteen miles our body temperature would be enough to make our blood literally boil.

As we continue our ascent the temperature unexpectedly begins to rise. This temperature increase, noticable between sixteen and thirty-two miles, puzzled scientists for a long time. To-day it is known that this warming up is caused by physico-chemical reactions. These reactions are connected with a very active part of the sunlight which the human eye cannot perceive. This ultra-violet light of very short wavelength, "ultra-violet C," shows its strength at this altitude, by splitting the molecules of oxygen each consisting of two atoms (O_2). The monatomic oxygen (O) thus formed is then converted by a process, which is only partially understood, into a new substance, the poisonous ozone (O_3) (from the Greek *ozein*: to smell). Each molecule of ozone is formed by the combination of three atoms of oxygen, and the heat liberated by this chemical process is sufficient to raise our thermometer to more than 30° C. at a height of 32 miles.

This high layer of ozone acts as a life saver: the ultra-violet rays lose much of their power in converting oxygen into ozone. This is just as well, for if these rays reached us at full strength, their penetrating and destructive power would cause grave biological damage. The ozone layer, therefore, acts as an umbrella spread out over the earth, safeguarding us from the most dangerous part of the ultra-violet rays.

The sky above us is now pitch black. The thermometer falls again to minus 70° C. Up here the air molecules are too far apart to transmit sound and a deathly silence surrounds us. If a space pilot with a message were to arrive at this moment, we would be able to see his lips moving but not to hear his voice. A glance downwards shows the surface of the earth to be indistinct. Cities, forests, mountains and seas have become a mosaic of grey, green and brown spots, while the clouds drift by like small pieces of cotton-wool. The horizon is distant and misty, and for the first time the curvature of the earth appears clearly against the black sky, giving us an idea of the immensity of our planet and the nameless power that keeps it suspended in space.

A glance at the dial of the instrument recording electric charges distracts our attention for a moment. We are now at a height of about fifty miles and the pointer has moved. The air is now electrically charged, which means that neutral air particles have changed their nature and are capable of attracting or repelling each other according to the character of their charge. We have penetrated the first of the four (or occasionally five) electric layers of the atmosphere.[1]

[1] According to Dr. Hildegard Kallmann of the University of California the ionosphere does not consist of several electrically charged layers. The whole ionosphere is filled with electrically charged particles whose density increases with height (see also the table on pages 20-21).

It is the so-called "D" layer, which only exists when the sun shines on it. As with so many of the atmosphere's secrets, we have no exact knowledge about the electric layers. The atomic physicists tell us, however, that the atom consists of a positively charged nucleus surrounded by circulating, negatively charged "electrons" in fixed orbits, after the manner of our planetary system. The atoms, of which all matter is composed, including the nitrogen and oxygen atoms outside our window, are constructed on this basic principle. Something strange has happened to the atoms up here, however. Tiny elementary particles and ultra-violet rays from the sun have attacked and changed their structure. The sun's rays have been sufficiently fierce to knock out some of the electrons from the electrically neutral system. When a neutral atom loses an electron the positive charge predominates and it becomes a positively charged "ion," while the electron is split off as a negatively charged elementary particle.

That, roughly speaking, is the situation we meet in the "D layer." Previously there were thought to be A, B and C layers as well, but these do not exist. There are further electric layers at greater heights,

$$\text{the } E^1 \text{ layer at about 60 miles.}$$
$$E^2 \text{ layer at about 80 miles.}$$
$$F^1 \text{ layer at about 140 miles.}$$
$$F^2 \text{ layer at about 200 miles.}$$

All these layers teem with positively and negatively charged atomic fragments and, when they were named, they were called the "ionosphere" (from the Greek *ion*: wandering).

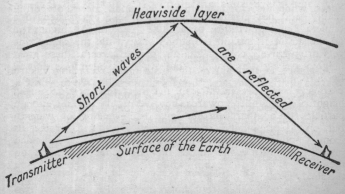

The electrically charged "Heaviside" layer reflects the short waves.

The ionosphere is a very interesting storey. In it appear the ghostly polar lights, about which we shall hear later. From this electrically charged zone radio waves are reflected back to earth as if from a mirror, if an electric storm due to sun spot activity does not "extinguish" one or other of the layers. The E layer (also called the Heaviside layer after its famous discoverer) enables radio technicians to cover great distances with their short-wave transmissions. As some radio short-waves only travel in straight lines one cannot receive them when the transmitter is below the horizon and covered by the curvature of the earth. If, however, these radio beams are directed upwards they are deflected by the Heaviside layer and overcome this curvature.

Our altimeter has now climbed to fifty-eight miles. The last clouds glide past us—hardly visible gossamer veils—probably made up of cosmic dust. They are the "noctilucent" clouds, which can occasionally be seen from earth during the morning or evening twilight when the sun is on, or even under, the horizon. Only then does the sunlight meet them at such an angle as to make them visible to us.

While we are still vainly trying to make out the shape or composition of these clouds a streak of lightning appears above us. It flashes past with a burning tail—a meteor. We have reached a height where the air is just dense enough to ignite these "bullets from outer space" by friction. Geophysicists have calculated that the atmosphere catches about one hundred million of these small stone splinters daily and makes them glow like shooting stars for a few seconds before rendering them harmless.

When we reach the 120-mile mark after two hours' travel our cabin has become an inferno. If we were up there in reality, and not in imagination, we would be roasted to a cinder. The temperature reads 800° C. and the higher we go the hotter it gets on the sunny side, while the shady side gets progressively colder. The air temperatures at these great heights are most unusual. What we call warmth is caused by a bombardment of air particles on our skin, the air particles being set in motion by the sun's rays. From a height of forty miles upwards, however, there are not enough particles to bombard us and give us a feeling of warmth but, on the other hand, the air is also too thin to protect us from the burning, direct rays of the sun. An unprotected man would burn away under the action of these rays on the sunny side of the cabin, while he would freeze solid on the shady side.

We have now taken four hours to reach a height of two hundred and forty miles, and have not yet reached the upper edge of the atmosphere. What surrounds us now is air spread incredibly thinly, but still air. This is the "exosphere" (from the Greek *exo*: outside), where the gravitational pull of the earth acts very weakly on the air particles. Their number is very small compared to lower layers but they move much faster. Under these circumstances some of them escape completely from the gravitational field of the earth to roam in outer space, until they reach the gravitational sphere of another star. Some of them may wander around the earth like tiny satellites, while others may dive back into the lower layers. This depends on the direction of their flight, and this again depends on their collisions with each other in an endless game of billiards. The exosphere is the uppermost storey of our atmosphere; above it begins outer space.

We have now risen through the aerial sea in one tremendous bound. We have penetrated the element without which no bird could fly, no man could breathe and no plant could blossom. Without the atmosphere the earth would be a desolate waste, like the surface of the moon, pitted by meteoric craters. We would lack the friendly glow of the evening campfire and the relief of rain after sultry weather. There would be no thunder or lightning, no rainbows and no clouds to change the face of the sky as if by magic. It is the air which tempers the searing heat of the sun to a bearable degree, and which prevents the stored-up warmth of the earth from escaping too quickly. Without our atmosphere all the water on earth would boil by day and freeze by night.

An even greater danger would be the penetrating rays of shorter wave-length from space which would hit the living cells of our skins and destroy them. Among the rays caught by the atmosphere are the space, or cosmic rays. Their origin and effects are not yet completely explained, but we have learnt a great deal about them since V. F. Hess discovered them in 1912. Cosmic rays are influenced by the earth's magnetic field and occur particularly frequently at the magnetic poles. They must, therefore, consist, at least partly, of electrically charged particles. It is certain that they possess more energy than any other form of radioactive emanation known to us, including those created by atomic explosions. The number of "hard" cosmic rays reaching the earth is too small to be dangerous to mankind, although some of them may penetrate the hereditary factors (chromosomes) and cause mutations. These rays can, after all, penetrate blocks of lead more than three feet thick. They have been detected a thousand feet below the surface of the earth and ten thousand feet below the level of the ocean. From what quarter of the universe do these eerie invaders come? Are they caused by sun spots? Do they originate in a super nova, one of those cosmic catastrophes when a fixed star explodes with an immense expenditure of light, giving off more energy in one day than our sun does in forty thousand years? We must confess that we do not know.

The ultra-violet rays, which we have already mentioned in connection with the ozone layer, are not quite so dangerous as the cosmic rays. Most of these are also caught by the atmosphere. Amongst the small amount that reaches us there are the long wave-length ultra-violet "A" and "B" rays which can be of value to man, if used with moderation, because they have a skin-browning and bactericidal action. The bio-physicist Carl Dorno has stated that the ultra-violet rays are like a surgeon's scalpel: "beneficial if used correctly, but fatal when employed indiscriminately." We should remember this when we expose our light-starved bodies to the sun once winter is over.

Warmth, light and ultra-violet rays are the gifts that the sun proffers us free of charge, day after day. It is up to us to make good use of them, for they are among the necessities of life. That we can make use of them, and not perish under them, is due to the invisible element above us of which Shakespeare makes Hamlet say:

> This most excellent canopy, the air

3

CLOUDS, RAINBOWS AND
SKY COLOURS

LIKE SO MUCH OF NATURE the air is an inexhaustible source of beauty. There is so much variety in its palette that any one pattern need not be repeated for thousands of years.

The scientist knows that the beauty of the sky is essentially no more than the interplay of atmospheric humidity and sunlight; only in exceptional circumstances do dust and ash particles colour the air. He knows that the moisture in conjunction with the light brings forth the various colours in the sky. If all the water present in the atmosphere as vapour, rain, ice, snow and hail were precipitated onto the earth, it would only cover it with a layer about one inch thick.

The ultimate source of atmospheric moisture is the sun, which causes a part of all the water on the earth to evaporate. An endless, invisible flow of water vapour rises to the sky from the lakes, rivers and seas, as well as from the soil, from plants and from animal bodies. In the sky the water is stored in three forms: as a colourless and odourless gas, in liquid form as finely dispersed, cloud-forming droplets and in solid form like ice, hail or snow.

The atmosphere cannot, however, absorb unlimited quantities of moisture; the amount depends mainly on the temperature. Thus two hundred cubic feet of air at 0° C. can only hold about an ounce of water vapour. A further increase—if the air is not completely pure—leads to inevitable condensation. This means that the water vapour changes into billions of minute droplets which make up the clouds. If the temperature falls below freezing point these droplets solidify into ice particles, giving rise to ice needles and platelets or star-shaped snow flakes, by further condensation of vapour. If the temperature falls below minus 35° C., water vapour can change directly to ice or snow crystals by "sublimation" without an intermediate liquid phase (the liquid phase would be of an immeasurably short duration).

Clouds usually consist either of droplets or of ice crystals, although both can exist together in the same cloud. As a rule droplet clouds can easily be distinguished from ice clouds by their appearance. If a cloud is composed exclusively or predominantly of droplets, its outline is sharply defined against the sky. The edges of ice-clouds, on the other hand, appear indistinct and frayed. The best examples of droplet-clouds are the different types of cumulus; those white, cotton-wool clouds of rounded, baroque form which can be seen solemnly drifting across the summer sky at 4000 to 6500 feet. Each one of them forms a sort of crown, the visible termination of an invisibly rising column of air which has been warmed by the ground. One can easily recognise cumulus clouds by their horizontal lower edges and the enormous cauliflowers seething above them. Sometimes they pile up to a height of four or five miles. In such cases the temperature in the upper parts of the cloud can fall to minus 20 or 40° C., when the droplets turn to ice. The visible sign of such ice formation is a fibrous, anvil-shaped structure rising high above the rest. When a cumulus cloud assumes this shape we can expect lightning and thunderstorms.

The anvil is only one form of ice cloud; the more typical examples are the feathery cirrus clouds. They occur at a height of about four to six miles and their shapes are reminiscent of Japanese paintings: barely visible, transparent forms appear either as spidery patterns of long threads sometimes ending in hooks or tufts, or else as groups of small high drifting puffs. They may swiftly vary in thickness, but all cirrus clouds appear white, because of the sunlight reflected from the edges of their ice crystals.

A third important group are the layer, or stratus clouds. When they occur, they often cover the whole sky in an unbroken blanket. Between these and the cirrus and cumulus clouds there is a whole range of mixed and intermediate forms. The milky-white cirro-stratus clouds, the grey-white alto-stratus clouds, drifting at a height of 6500–20,000 feet, and the grey snow and rain clouds (nimbo-stratus). There are also some further types which are of importance to the meteorologist, because he can make deductions about the weather from their occurrence.

The air contains tiny salt, ash and dust particles as well as cloud-forming droplets and ice crystals. All of them introduce turbid elements, hence a ray of light penetrating the air may be influenced in various ways by meeting one of them. It can be bent or scattered; in other words the particles can deflect the ray from its original course, and frequently separate it into its component colours. On the other hand the ray can be absorbed by the particles which cause turbidity, and in these circumstances heat can sometimes be generated. Independent of all these possibilities is the fact that visibility decreases when the number of opaque, turbidity-causing particles increases. A stroll in a fog will easily demonstrate this. The component colours of sunlight are not equally affected by the usual mist or the very fine dry fog. We already know that sunlight is a mixture of colours, and that white daylight is not pure and fundamental but is composed of the basic rainbow hues; also that the short-waved blue rays are most easily deflected from their straight paths and tend to wander aimlessly in the atmosphere. Physicists say that they are more easily "scattered" by the finest air particles and fog droplets than the yellow and red rays. This causes the red rays from a source of light to penetrate farther than the blue ones.

The technician who invented the fog lamp took this fact into account. The yellowish light given off by the lamp is scarcely affected by the fog droplets and penetrates far into the mist. These lamps can, however, only fulfill their purpose in a fine, smoky, dry fog. In a real "pea-souper" the best fog lamp is comparatively useless, for a wet fog consists of larger drops which interfere equally with all the coloured components of white light. Even the sun appears only as an indistinct, milky disc through the curtain of a wet fog, whereas it is red in the fine haze of the evening sky.

Sun and fog occasionally play curious tricks when they join forces to deceive mountaineers. On foggy mountainsides the "Brocken spectre" may appear in the vicinity of the astonished climber. It was given this name because it was first observed at the Brocken in the Harz mountains. While climbing a steep cliff it may happen that the mountaineer suddenly sees a ghostly companion above, below or beside him. This is his own enormously enlarged shadow, ringed with colours, which the sun has cast on a fog bank drifting past him. The fright caused by this apparition has brought many experienced climbers into serious danger.

We have already mentioned the dispersal of light rays several times, but it has not been explained. The process is fairly complicated, and to understand it completely a thorough grounding in optics is required. We will, therefore, only give a few examples of light dispersal by water droplets in the air. These droplets act like glass spheres which throw back the light ray or break it into its spectrum of component colours. A well-known example of this is the rainbow. A rainbow occurs when the sun behind the observer shines on a rain cloud or on falling rain. In these circumstances we usually see the "primary rainbow." Even if only a part of it is visible the outer edge glows red, followed by yellow, green, blue and violet as the eye travels downwards. Often the rainbow does not stand alone above the rainy landscape. Like a ghostly reflection in a mirror a "secondary rainbow" with a reversed colour sequence sometimes rises above it.

The French philosopher Descartes (1596–1650) already had a fair idea of the origin of the rainbow's colours. According to his conception a section of the sun's rays enter the side of the raindrop facing the viewer and are reflected by the farther side of the drop to emerge again frontally and laterally. This breaks the rays into the colours of the rainbow. The observer perceives that part of the arc lying at a visual angle of about 42 and about 50 degrees as red, followed upwards or downwards by yellow, green and blue in that order (see diagram). In the droplets of the secondary rainbow the rays are reflected four times and therefore lose more of their luminous power. For this reason the secondary rainbow usually only appears sketchily above the primary one.

Few people know the great diversity of forms in which rainbows can appear. They may be wide or narrow. The

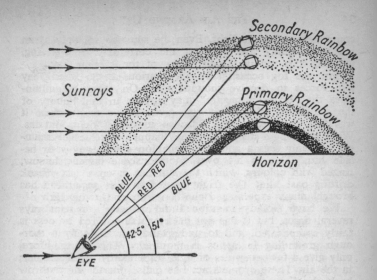

The origin of the rainbow. For greater clarity only one drop is shown in the relevant part.

varying width of the colour bands and their altered sequence may give an indication of the size of droplet causing them. These are the eerie secondary rainbows and, if you are lucky, you may even see a moon rainbow, the luminosity of which is so feeble that the colour sequence can barely be distinguished.

Besides rainbows there are other spectral phenomena which appear in the sky, such as the coronas around the sun and moon which have given rise to many superstitions. While the sun's corona can seldom be seen because of its overwhelming brightness, the moon's is very distinct when, after a clear day, a thin veil of stratus cloud lies above the earth. The moon then appears to be set in a bright, faintly blue field with a shimmering reddish-yellow circular edge. Surrounding this reddish hem are concentric coloured rings, first green, then blue. When the droplets are all the same size we can see further rings with a rainbow-like colour sequence, but of decreasing intensity and sharpness.

The "haloes" on the other hand are phenomena of pure reflection and refraction. They are narrow white rings with red edges which appear around the sun and moon when the air is filled with the microscopic ice crystals of cirro-stratus clouds. If one were to place one point of a pair of com-

35

passes in the centre of such a ring and the other one on the circumference, the angle between the two arms would be 22, or more rarely 46°, 90°, 120° and other degrees. These rings can lie in different planes and intersect each other. At the intersections there appear bright spots called "mock suns" and "mock moons." These solar and lunar apparitions can themselves be adorned with coloured wreaths. The wreaths are caused by the separation of light into its component parts by the refractive action of the ice crystals.

The solar and lunar haloes are more frequently seen in polar regions than in our latitudes. The Scandinavians, for instance, are not particularly surprised when up to six mock suns appear in the sky at one time; two each on either side of the sun and one each above and below. On the 12th of March, 1956, the citizens of Hamburg saw a particularly splendid halo. The sky above the city was covered by a fine veil of ice cloud and the sun appeared in triple form surrounded by two beautiful, shining rings. The sunny, long-lasting summer which northern peoples like to predict from such omens did not, however, materialise, for the summer of 1956 was one of the rainiest in several decades.

More rarely seen than the coronas and haloes are the mother-of-pearl clouds. They are iridescent formations in the stratosphere, and their highly coloured lustre is clearly visible in the centre as well as at the transparent edges. In Southern Norway mother-of-pearl clouds usually appear when a deep depression is lying north of Oslo, but this alone does not help to explain their origin. The American meteorologist Humphreys believes that an exchange of stratospheric currents from the equator to the pole and vice versa plays an important part in their formation. They have very different shapes; sometimes they are gossamer thin, at others comparatively thick, but they always attract attention by their remarkable polychromatic appearance. The Norwegian author Sigrid Undset once described a mother-of-pearl cloud as follows: "The northern silhouette . . . was extraordinarily clear. Against the golden centre the cloud changed colour in an infinite variety of red-violet, lilac-pink, red and orange tones. Up towards the zenith and downwards in a southerly direction its contours appeared as if blown away by the wind—and surrounded by a fan-shaped, turquoise green, gold-rimmed field it slowly vanished into the air. . . ."

A very rare and curious phenomenon, the cause of which is as yet incompletely known, is the "green flash." It is seen above the horizon for only a few moments at sunrise, or more frequently at sundown. Those who have visited the island of Ischia will know that the green flash can occasionally be seen when looking across the sea towards Forio. It occurs mostly in the sub-tropics when visibility is good, and it is probably caused by a peculiar form of light refraction. When the sun is below the horizon the rays from its upper edge strike the thick layer of air around the earth, and the green light rays are deflected for a moment so that they run along the earth's crust and so reach our eyes for a short while. The blue rays are so dispersed that they do not interfere and the red and yellow rays are not deflected sufficiently to rise above the horizon. According to Dietze the green flash occurs most frequently when atmospheric conditions favour mirages.

The effects that the sun displays at sunset are amongst the most beautiful that the air can afford us, yet the splendour of colour is caused simply by the dust particles deflecting and dispersing the sunlight.

Even before the sun sinks below the horizon it is noticeable that the colours of the clear sky become more saturated. While the light glows reddish-yellow around the sun and yellow-green near the horizon, the blue overhead deepens. When the sun stands only one or two degrees above the horizon it pours a blazing flood along the edge of the earth. The yellow turns to orange and finally to a fiery or even blood-red glow. When it has sunk from sight a purple tint appears in the western sky, which reaches its greatest intensity when the sun is five degrees below the horizon. Then a semi-circle of pink deepening to purple, separated from the horizon by a narrow brown-red band, lingers above the place where it has disappeared. This is caused mainly by dust particles reflecting sunrays at a height of six to twelve miles, and disappears as soon as the sun has sunk about seven degrees below the horizon. Now darkness falls and the day is over. Twilight in the popular sense of the word has ended when it is no longer possible to read a newspaper on a clear evening. The scientist does not accept the legibility of newsprint as a measure and "astronomic" twilight only begins when the sun is eighteen degrees below the horizon and stars of the fifth magnitude—those which can just be seen with the naked eye—become visible.

Long after the sun has set for the inhabitants of the plains, its rays still fall on the atmosphere. They create the Alpine glow on mountain tops and with their purple light illuminate the rare, bluish-white noctilucent clouds at a height of 50 miles. According to the theory of F. H. Ludlam of the Imperial College of Science and Technology, London, these clouds do not consist of tiny ice particles but possibly of dust of volcanic, meteoric or interstellar origin.

On exceptional occasions active volcanoes can also play an impressive part in colouring the atmosphere. A remarkable example of this was given by the eruption of Krakatoa on the 26th and 27th of August, 1883. During this cataclysm about four and a half cubic miles of stone were thrown into the air. Rocks the size of a man's head were hurled upwards with an initial velocity of 2000 to 3300 feet per second, and the thunder could be heard on the island of Madagascar, nearly three thousand miles away. For days the sky was darkened. The finest ash particles ejected by the volcano rose to a height of fifty miles. Here they were caught by air currents and carried several times around the globe. For months afterwards they caused fantastic sky colourations, such as dawns and sunsets of exceptional splendour, as if Nature was penitent for the sixty-three thousand deaths caused by the disaster. The sun appeared in a variety of colours, even copper-red and green. An eye witness spoke of a glow from the sunset "as if from white-hot steel" reddening while rising to the zenith and then changing to blue. "From the zenith it spread outward in a most splendid green . . . clouds of burning gold, copper and silver crossed the firmament." Even blue suns occurred, like those seen on rare occasions in Europe when forest fires rage in Canada and the west winds carry the finest ash particles over our continent.

All these colours, from whatever source, have one thing in common: they cannot be imitated by human means. However often we may try to capture them on canvas, paper, wood, metal or any other medium, we shall always fail. The immeasurable variety, ranging from the delicacy of a misty landscape to the deep, saturated colours of a sunset, are the work of a master who has truly "heavenly" resources. His brush is the sunlight and his canvas the restless ether—no painter can ever possess these.

4

MIRAGES

ON A WINDLESS DAY IN CUXHAVEN (the seaport of Hamburg) a little boy ran home and shouted excitedly: "Mother, an island is falling from the sky!" His mother's unbelieving smile vanished when she looked out of the window for there, in front of her startled eyes, hung the island of Heligoland diagonally above her house, head downwards. The red cliffs were unmistakable and the dunes and other details clearly visible. There it hung suspended, as if held by a giant hand and about to come crashing down any moment. Luckily the island did not fall and the child's fears disappeared when the phantom vanished towards evening.

Another atmospheric spectre once puzzled and deluded men for nearly a century. In 1818 the English brothers James and John Ross set out to find the famous "Northwest Passage," the sea-way linking the Pacific and Atlantic oceans along the northern coast of North America. North of Baffin Island in Canada they entered unknown waters, and when they went on deck one morning they found their passage blocked by huge mountains. Thinking that they had sailed up a blind alley they turned about and reported that the Northwest Passage did not exist. The American admiral Robert Peary also admitted defeat when he met this same barrier seventy-five years or so later. "We saw the mountains and called them 'Crocker Land,'" was all that he could report on his return.

By now curiosity had been aroused. What lay behind these peculiar mountains? Did they conceal ore deposits, or gold? Did unknown tribes live there? Adventurers and explorers from all over the world tried to solve the mystery, but the road to Crocker Land was long and difficult. Only after the American Museum of Natural History had donated 300,000 dollars could a new expedition which stood any chance of success be started. Donald MacMillan, the leader of the expedition, was the hero of the hour, but his journey in 1913 turned out to be one of the most disappointing explorations of our time.

Where Peary had seen mountains MacMillan found only a watery waste. Where according to Peary there were deep and wide channels, floes of pack-ice threatened his ship. Finally Crocker Land appeared, but to the astonishment of the crew it lay two hundred miles farther west than Peary had stated. MacMillan sailed on as far as possible; then he dropped anchor and set out on foot with a team of picked men. When they tried to approach the mountains, however, the mountains moved backward. If they stood still, the mountains stood still as well. When they started again the mountains receded once more. There they were, the glaciers and snowfields glittering in the polar sunlight, with dark valleys promising mineral wealth.

The men redoubled their efforts. Finally they got so near to a valley, enclosed on three sides by mountains, that they felt certain of success. Just at that moment the sun sank below the horizon and all the hills and valleys dissolved as if by magic. Dumbfounded the men looked at each other. They were surrounded by ice, ice in all directions, as far as the eye could see. Not a hill or a mountain was in sight. They stood in the pale green arctic twilight, the victims of one of the greatest practical jokes the air has ever played on man.

"Mirage" is the name physicists give to all types of optical illusion that are due to atmospheric conditions. The details have not yet all been explained, but we know enough to have a very good idea of their origin.

Mirages occur most frequently when there is a layer of very warm or very cold air above the ground. Let us, for instance, imagine a desert where the sun has warmed the sand. Immediately above the ground there is a cushion of hot air which is optically thinner than the higher and colder layers, that is to say, the light rays move more easily through it than through cold air. For reasons which we will explain later the light is refracted several times, which means that it is bent or reflected as if the boundary between the air layers were a mirror.

Let us imagine a field, crossed by a tarmac road, with the loose soil touching the tarmac on either side. If we were to mount a tractor and drive across the field so as to meet the tarmac at an acute angle, what would happen when the leading front wheel mounted the tarmac? It would meet less resistance than the other front wheel which was still in the loose soil. One wheel would go quickly forward while the other braked, and since the wheels are connected by the front axle the tractor would slew round and we would find ourselves back in the field unless we turned the steering-wheel frantically. A light ray in the desert behaves just like the tractor; when it falls diagonally through the cold air into the hot air cushion it is turned around before meeting the ground.

Now for a concrete example. A man is standing on a sand dune somewhere in the desert. There is a group of palm trees on a second dune several hundred yards away, and in between the two dunes there is a lake of hot air, warmed by the desert sand. In such a situation the observer will see two groups of palm trees, one in the usual manner by direct vision across the intervening air and another, inverted, below the first. The reasons for this are as follows: the light rays which make the palms visible come from all directions in space. Those rays travelling from one dune to the other above the hot air lake give the first picture. Those, on the other hand, which travel diagonally downward from the trees into the heated air below behave just like the tractor in the field. They are bent and deflected upwards, meeting the eye of the observer from below. It is as if a mirror was lying on the floor of the desert showing an inverted reflection of

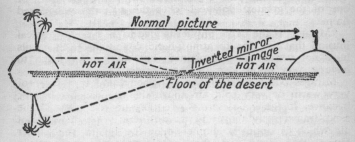

The desert type of mirage. The palms are seen double, once directly above the mirror of hot air and once below the true picture. At the same time the hot air reflects a piece of sky, giving the impression of water.

the palms. At the same time a piece of sky is also reflected in the hot shimmering air, giving the impression of a sheet of water in which groups of palms are standing, some upright and some head downwards.

Car drivers encounter such atmospheric tricks on a smaller scale when they see puddles on hot, dry summer roads. The puddles are merely pieces of sky reflected by the hot air above the tarmac. They disappear as one approaches and cause no more damage than that advancing cars seem to swim in them. Wanderers in the desert, on the other hand, have been driven mad by such false waters. These waters are not figments of the imagination or hallucinations, but genuine mirror-reflections, created by the air. "Bahr el Shaitan" the Arabs call them, "Lakes of Satan."

There is a tragic story told by the inhabitants of Cochise County in Arizona. In the neighbourhood of Hado Flats there is a ten-mile lake lying along the railway. This lake is visible summer and winter, although it is only really there in winter. During summer the hot reflecting air above the lake bed merely gives the illusion of water. A pilot who knew the lake from a winter journey tried to land a seaplane on it during the summer. As he began his landing the phantom disappeared; the machine disintegrated and the pilot died of his injuries.

When the boundary between the hot and cold air is uneven, the mirrored objects are frequently distorted. Roy Chapman Andrews, the American explorer of Asia, thought he was dreaming when he once saw fabulous animals like huge swans wading in a lake in the Gobi desert. From a few hundred yards away they seemed to be gigantic creatures from another world, wandering around on stilt-like legs nearly fifteen feet high. Andrews at once asked the expedition's artist to make drawings of these unusual beasts. He himself approached the lake stealthily, but the water shrank as he got nearer and its inhabitants changed their shape to the same degree. It was an alarming, clearly visible process. The plump giant swans became slender antelopes grazing peacefully on the sparse desert vegetation. A hot air layer had produced the impression of water and the unevenness of the layer had grotesquely distorted the animals' bodies.

On the 11th of April, 1916, during an Anglo-Turkish engagement in World War I, a mirage forced the English Artillery to stop firing. An illusory landscape appeared before their eyes and completely masked the enemy's position. The English Commander's report contained the remarkable sentence "Temporary cease-fire because of mirage."

Napoleon's army had encountered mirages previously in Egypt in 1798. When they saw landscapes standing on their heads, vanishing lakes and blades of grass turning into palm

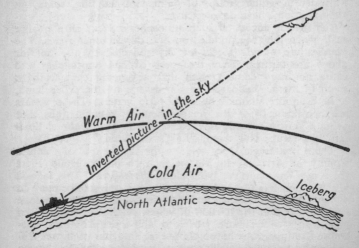

The polar type of mirage occurs on cold seas. The reflecting layer of warm air lies high above the observer. An iceberg lying beyond the horizon can thus appear to be hanging head downwards in the sky.

trees, they fell on their knees and prayed to be saved from the impending end of the world. Only one of them kept his head and considered these phenomena, the French physicist Gaspard Monge. He was, eventually, the first to find an explanation for these desert-type mirages by exposing the hot air layers above the desert as the culprits.

A different sort of mirage is the polar type, which occurs when the air immediately above the ground is very cold and there is a warmer layer above it. The observer then sees the inverted picture of a distant object high in the sky. Sometimes there are even two pictures. When, for instance, ships or icebergs are floating in a calm sea they create a mirror image in the cold water below them. If the observer looks in just the right direction he will see both the object and the reflection in the warm upper layers of the air. A famous case of such a "double exposure" occurred in the Antarctic in 1912. A survivor of Captain Scott's South Polar Expedition reports that the men on their return to the coast saw the mother ship *Terra Nova* hanging in the sky in double form. There was an inverted picture of the sailing ship, with an upright one above it and smoke was drifting upwards and down-

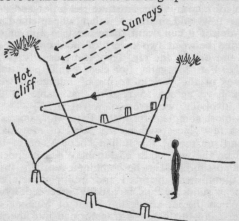

The sun has warmed a cliff. The air above the stone has grown hotter than that surrounding it and reflects the light. When this rare type of mirage occurs the observer can see what lies round the bend of the road.

wards from the cook-house chimneys. The ship itself was still hidden by intervening hills, but its mirage, far away, showed that all was well on board.

In the First World War a German submarine commander

surfaced near the American coast, and on looking through his periscope saw the skyscrapers of New York hanging above him. They seemed about to dive, roof downwards, into the sea, and the mariner is said to have turned tail and run.

Parisians tell of a bewildering trick that the air sometimes plays on their city. Conditions for the polar type of mirage occasionally occur above the French capital. Then it happens that the Eiffel Tower entertains the citizens by balancing an inverted image of itself upside down.

We have already mentioned that mirages do not always reflect an object in its true shape. It can be enlarged, contracted or distorted like a picture in the hall of mirrors at a fair, according to the position and nature of the refracting air layers. A drifting floe in the Arctic may become a dangerous iceberg, a palm tree shrink to a blade of grass and a fishing hut swell into a palace. In mountains one can even have reflections round the corner. A wanderer in the North American mountains is said to have been saved from a bear which was hiding around a bend in the road by a vertical layer of hot air in front of a cliff giving warning in time.

The most famous, although very rare, form of mirage is the Fata Morgana. It demonstrates the polar and desert types simultaneously and, perhaps, other unexplained reflections as well. Before it can occur there must be a layer of cold air sandwiched between two layers of hot, one just above the ground and one in the air. The Arabs usually call all types of mirages Fata Morgana. For clearer differentiation between the causes of the various forms of mirage, however, most scientists have agreed to restrict that name to those phenomena involving two layers of warm air.

In its most complete form the Fata Morgana can only be seen in a few places such as the Strait of Messina (between Sicily and the toe of the Italian "boot"), or in the bay of Toyama on the west coast of Japan. When it appears all imaginable possibilities can be combined, upright, inverted, enlarged, diminished, distorted and multiple pictures. It does not appear suddenly but is usually preceded by a ghostly cloud. When the air above the Strait of Messina is hot and the water calm this cloud is transformed into the image of a splendid harbour town. A second town appears and piles up above it, and yet a third, with shining towers and palaces. Sometimes it seems as if the houses lie below the water, and if one looks closely one can see the inhabitants strolling through the streets in billowing white garments.

The complicated reflections causing the Fata Morgana in the Strait of Messina remain unexplained to this day. Some observers believe that it is only a reflection of the Sicilian harbour of Messina; others say they recognise a strip of coast line, the trees and stones of which have been magnified and distorted. A third theory mentions an Italian fishing village, transformed into a beautiful town by the mirroring air. Whatever its cause may be, the Fata Morgana remains an indescribably beautiful aerial effect. Though it greatly exceeds all other types of mirage in variety, like all the rest it is only caused by the action of the sun on the earth and the air.

5

POLAR LIGHTS

ABOUT A HUNDRED OR TWO HUNDRED THOUSAND YEARS AGO the original inhabitants of the earth began to leave the warmer regions and occupied the colder areas in the north and south of our planet. Here they were surprised by a strange phenomenon. At night a silent, phantom spectacle appeared high above their heads. It was a glow in the sky, an eerie light which they had never seen before. Sometimes it was white, sometimes faintly tinted with green or red; sometimes it hung unmoving above the horizon and sometimes it flamed up in a wild variety of colours towards the zenith. The light could take on a multitude of shapes: glowing domes, coronas or clouds, glistening curtains, flashing bands or glittering diadems came and went, pulsated and flickered in the night-blue sky. However much they speculated, the newcomers could find no explanation for these strange manifestations.

Their imagination was stimulated. Superstitions and sagas began to surround the Polar Lights. They imagined that gods with flaming torches were locked in bitter combat, or that these lights were a warning by the Earth Spirit of the impending end of the world. The Eskimos in Hudson Bay believe to this day that the polar lights are lanterns with which demons are searching the universe for lost souls. The Nordic sagas say that they are the reflection from the golden shields on which the Walkyries carry the souls of fallen heroes to Valhalla.

What really lies behind these celestial fireworks?

The polar lights (called "Northern" and "Southern" in their respective hemispheres) are caused by an invisible and silent cosmic bombardment. Their origin is a hail of tiny solar missiles, to which the earth is exposed in the same way as it is to the endless stream of sunlight.

The sun shoots tiny pieces of its own substance into space. These are hydrogen atoms, disintegrated by the heat of the sun into positively charged hydrogen nuclei (protons) and negatively charged elementary particles (electrons). It is only during the last few years that astonomers have discovered that the sun probably has three types of "firing range" on its glowing surface from which these particles are discharged. One type consists of incandescent gaseous eruptions—flaming "solar torches"—found close to the large sun spots. A second type consists of glowing fountains of gas (spicules), but these are smaller and are distributed about the whole surface of the sun in great numbers. Offshoots of the sun, which play an important part in the creation of these small missiles, make up the third type. These offshoots are masses of gas thrown out from the body of the sun, and consist mainly of hydrogen, helium and calcium. They are ejected to a height above the surface of the sun equal to 2.6 times the distance from the earth to the moon. Under the influence of the sun's strong magnetic field, the particles race away into space at a speed of 600 to 1200 miles a second, and take on an average twenty-six hours to reach the earth. Since the sun and its magnetic field revolve, just like the earth, the paths of these "corpuscular streams," as they are called, are bundled together and slightly curved, like the jets of water from a rotating lawn sprinkler.

What happens when the earth comes within the range of these small projectiles? Perhaps we had better ask the question: what would happen if these solar bullets reached the earth? The answer to that is quite simple. They would descend on us like a cloudburst, and their powers of penetration would cause untold damage. Luckily this does not happen. The world is protected from them by an invisible barrier, the earth's magnetic field. Each one of us has held a compass and seen that the needle always points northwards. It is forced to do this by an invisible magnetic power emanating from the earth. It is not going too far to compare our globe to a single, huge magnet. This magnet has a (south-magnetic) pole in the north and a (north-magnetic) pole in the south, lying about 78 degrees north and 70 degrees west, and 78 degrees south and 111 degrees east respectively. If one connects these poles by an imaginary straight line one obtains the earth's magnetic axis. This axis runs directly through the centre of the earth and forms an angle of about twelve degrees with the geographic axis (running from the North to the South pole). The magnetic axis forms the nucleus of the earth's strong magnetic field. If a giant sprinkled iron filings from an enormous salt cellar into the space

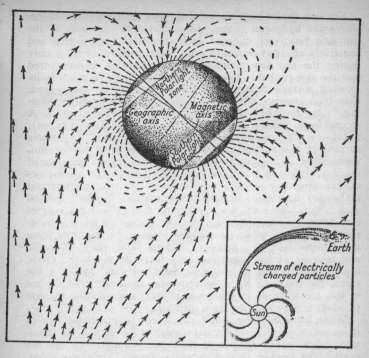

The origin of Polar lights: electrically charged particles from the sun are deflected by the earth's lines of magnetic force (arrows). Coming from the ring current (see text) they enter the zones of polar lights and stimulate the molecules in the atmosphere. These begin to glow under the bombardment, like the molecules of gas in a neon light tube. *Below right:* In streams (because of the magnetic field of the sun) and on a curved course (because of the rotation of the sun) the charged electric particles fly out into space. Some of them reach the earth.

around the globe, those filings that did not fall on to the earth would orientate themselves along the lines of magnetic force, and would form numerous large arcs above the earth (roughly as if the degrees of longitude had been stretched outwards). The earth would appear as if suspended inside a huge, spherical bird cage, the bars of which (lines of magnetic force) entered it in a ring around the magnetic poles (see diagram). This imaginary cage is the barrier which catches the solar particles and, as we shall see later, also deflects them.

Let us follow a shower of these electrically charged particles from the sun. What happens to them? According to the theory of the astronomers Störmer, Martyn, Chapman and Ferraro, the powerful terrestrial magnet at first forces the small particles into a "ring current," which encircles the earth around the equator at a height of about eighteen thousand miles. Here the protons from the sun circle rapidly from east to west in an invisible stream. A portion of them, however, follow the lines of magnetic force (the bars of the birdcage), being pulled earthwards near the magnetic poles and meeting the atmosphere with undiminished force. About sixty to ninety miles above our heads a barrage of literally annihilating force meets the rarefied oxygen and nitrogen of the upper air in the polar light zones. The gas molecules are shattered by the collision. They become "ionised," like the solar hydrogen atoms, and split into positive nuclei and negative electrons. Physicists call this "collision ionisation."

This process contains the essential secrets of the origin of the polar lights. Years of detailed research, mainly by Norwegian, Finnish and American scientists, have led to its elucidation. We do not understand all the details even to-day, but we can already form a fair picture of how collision ionisation can lead to the appearance of polar light.

According to Professor Meinel of the University of Chicago who has carried out particularly notable research on this subject, polar lights are caused in two different ways: either the electrons displaced from the oxygen and nitrogen atoms spring back into their original positions, or the positively charged solar missiles themselves combine with electrons.

According to the theory of Gartlein, Nichols and Booker there is a simultaneous appearance of "light effects along the lines of magnetic force of the earth." These scientists believe that the light is composed of thousands of rays each of them lasting barely a second. These short-lived rays are over a mile long and have a diameter of about three hundred feet, forming pillars of electrically charged air. They appear so close together that they give the impression of a glittering, quivering curtain in the sky. The glowing red and yellow-green light is caused by oxygen, the orange, blue-green and violet by nitrogen.

The close connection between the earth's magnetic power and polar lights is affirmed by the positions in which they are best seen. Contrary to popular opinion the lights do not increase as we approach the poles themselves. The best and most frequent examples occur in two belt-shaped zones towards the north and south. These belts are about three hundred miles wide and circle the globe at a certain distance from the magnetic poles. The Northern zone runs from the northern tip of the Norwegian mainland over Iceland to Southern Greenland and touches Alaska and the north Siberian coast. The Southern belt lies partially over the Antarctic continent and partially over the Indian ocean. On either side of these two zones there is a steady decrease in the frequency of the lights, and in Central Europe they are already as rare as at the magnetic North Pole.

Polar lights become particularly impressive and reach the luminosity of the half-moon when there are large and frequent sun spots, which happens about every eleven years. The connection is easily understood because, as we know, the sun ejects unusually forceful streams of electrically charged particles at such times. (The next maximum should occur in 1968.) When such energy-laden particles approach the earth the "ring current" swells like a spring tide. As a consequence, its own field of energy (which is fairly strong) increases in strength and confuses the earth's magnetic field. The lines of force become bent and "dented," and the polar lights grow stronger and appear in regions where they are not normally seen. Geophysicists say "a magnetic storm rages across the earth." These conditions inconvenience radio technicians. The interference in their trans-oceanic short-wave connections can make communication impossible. In New York a magnetic storm once played havoc with radio programmes. An intimate telephone conversation unaccountably reached the transmitter and was relayed to numerous listeners. When, during the last war, President Roosevelt wanted to speak urgently to Sir Winston Churchill on the other side of the Atlantic, the White House telephone operator found herself reiterating "But this is a personal call from the President himself!" into the indifferent ear of a raging magnetic storm.

It is easy to calculate the height of the polar lights in the sky by taking two simultaneous photographs from different positions. The picture of the light is then seen against a "grid" of stars, but each is slightly displaced. If the distance between the two positions is known, the amount of displacement forms the basis of the calculation. Many thousand photographs, taken over a number of years, have given us a very good idea of the height of the polar lights. They occur most frequently at sixty to ninety miles above the earth, which is approximately the height of the electrically charged "Heaviside" or E-layer of the atmosphere. Only in exceptional cases do they reach a height of up to six hundred miles. The lowest measured altitude of a polar light was less than forty miles, about seven times the height of Mount Everest.

It is not so easy to classify the different forms of polar light at all exactly. There are many intermediate and mixed types, and the personal opinion of the man making the classification is also involved. The American, Gartlein, differentiates twelve types, but the Finnish scientist, Sucksdorff, considers three sufficient:

1. The calm, evenly shining arcs. These are the most frequent and stretch fairly evenly from East to West. They have a sharp lower edge, but the upper limit is indistinct. They appear regularly in the polar light zones even when the earth is not exposed to magnetic storms.

2. The mobile forms, or "polar light eruptions." These include all ray-like forms and all figures of rapidly changing shape. This type is always coloured, usually blue-green. The luminosity varies and the maximum is reached shortly before midnight. When such lights occur the magnetic field of the earth is disturbed.

3. The "flaming" polar lights. These are very rare and occur only in connection with the polar light eruptions. Sucksdorff himself describes them as follows: "The flames are a magnificent spectacle and completely without colouration. They begin when the polar light eruption itself has 'burnt out.' Suddenly the whole sky seems to be in upheaval. It is as if mighty waves of light were racing from horizon to zenith. This display can last for hours. During it the magnetic field is always strongly disturbed."

No painter, photographer or film cameraman has been able to capture the real splendour of a polar light. Its full beauty is only unfolded in its movement and our colour films are not sensitive enough to show this. All we can do is to look.

6

PLANTS AND ANIMALS
CONQUER THE AIR

PLANTS MUST ALREADY HAVE EXISTED ON OUR PLANET about two thousand million years ago, when the air contained little or no free oxygen. In the first chapter we mentioned that they can only have been plants that were not so dependent on oxygen as those of to-day. These extremely primitive organisms already had useful properties; they could take in the abundant atmospheric carbon dioxide and use it for their metabolism.

The basic chemical process of plants, in which leaf pigments play a part, has become more specialised over millions of years. This is the mystery of assimilation, the incorporation of alien substances into the living body, which confronted and puzzled scientists for a long time. Only in 1779, when the botanist Ingen-Housz discovered that light is involved in this process, did they begin to reach an explanation. A plant manages to obtain nourishment from the air with the aid of sunlight. Experiments show that it does so by combining six molecules of carbon dioxide and six molecules of water, and using 674,000 calories of solar energy; it turns them into one molecule of grape sugar and six molecules of oxygen. This combination of substances in the presence of sunlight is called "photosynthesis." Using chemical symbols it runs as follows:

$$6 \ CO_2 + 6 \ H_2O + 674,000 \ \text{calories} = C_6H_{12}O_6 + 6 \ O_2.$$

This equation does not mean very much by itself. What does it tell us? That a certain amount of substances were changed and that this required a certain amount of solar energy. Quite so. What else does the formula offer? Does it explain the details involved in this change? It does not, and it is just these details which interest modern science most.

Work began again using the equation as a basis for new calculations, and fresh experiments were started. New and more specific questions arose: how was it possible that a tree of about ten tons dry weight could contain about five tons of carbon which, in their turn, had come from one hundred and forty million cubic feet of air? How was it possible that fifteen square feet of green leaf surface could take about six grains of carbon from the air, and in sixty seconds turn it into grape sugar, and finally into about thirteen grains of starch?

It was not easy to coax these secrets from Nature. Only in 1955 did the work of the American botanist Daniel Arnon begin to do so. Basing his work on previous experiments, Arnon was the first man to remove the granules containing the green pigment chlorophyll (chloroplasts) from the leaves of plants and, with their aid, to imitate photosynthesis in a test tube. He found that the isolated whole chloroplasts are, so to speak, miniature factories for photosynthesis. He also demonstrated something really astounding, namely that the pigments are not dependent on their hosts, the plant cells, since the little factories function splendidly without them.

The chloroplasts can perform the decisive operations of making sugar and starch from carbon dioxide and water even outside the plant. They do not hurry over this, however, but subdivide their labour. Arnon found that three distinct reactions make up the whole process, and that three vitamins play the roles of catalysts; this means that they make the chemical process possible by their mere presence, without being changed themselves. The vitamins are B_6, K and C.

Professor Arnon's experiments made it possible, for the first time, to change carbon dioxide and water into sugar and starch in the presence of sunlight, without the aid of living cells. We cannot yet judge the full significance of this, but we do know that if it becomes possible to repeat the experiment on an industrial scale, we will be independent of the usual methods of obtaining sugar and starch from plants. We could then, if we ever reach that stage, with the help of chlorophyll and sunlight, get part of our food literally out of thin air.

The air not only helps plants obtain their nourishment, it is also used by many of them for dispersal and reproduction. In spring and summer it is a vital means of transport for countless tiny germs, for pollen dust and for seeds and fruit. The wind will carry these small structures for varying distances, according to their flying and gliding capacity, dropping them to earth somewhere to start new growths. The efficiency of this method of transport is shown by the fact that tiny green algæ have been found at a height of six thousand feet, and almost weightless bacteria even up to a height of over eighteen thousand feet above the earth. One suburb of Berlin started a colony of orchids whose nearest neighbours were ninety miles away. Who has not seen the dandelion clocks, the tiny parachutes of which are carried in all directions by the wind? Who, as a child, has not chased after the spirally gliding sycamore seeds? Nature resorts to all kinds of tricks to ensure as wide a distribution as possible. Among the plants with aerial dispersal alone, there are three main types of dispersal, each with a different method of flight:

1. Dust-like seeds easily blown by the wind owing to their lightness (e.g. orchids).
2. Seeds or fruits with disc-like or wing-like structures (e.g. sycamores or ash trees).
3. Seeds or fruits with hairs or fluff which float like parachutes (e.g. dandelions).

What is true of plants also applies to animals. Three-quarters of all land-living forms of the animal kingdom have conquered the air, the insects in particular. They existed long before birds appeared, and have had many millions of years more to perfect their powers of flight. The fossils of the first flying insects are judged to be 230 million years old. The wings of these little animals stuck out stiffly from their bodies but, like all later insects' wings, they were already composed of two layers of chitin, the light, resistant material which makes up the insect skeleton. Insects' wings are extrusions of the skin, and have nothing in common with the "arms" which are the wings of birds and bats. Instead of bones the insects' wings have ribs which are filled with a colourless body fluid. Movement is caused by powerful muscles in the chest of the animal. The strength of these muscles is almost incredible. A slow-motion camera taking more than fifteen thousand pictures a second has demonstrated how rapidly they can move the wings. A bee, for instance, has one hundred and ninety wing-beats per second and a mosquito as many as three hundred.

The acrobats of the air are the dragonflies. With their two pairs of wings they achieve a manœuvrability which our aeroplanes have tried in vain to imitate. They can remain motionless in the air, shoot forward with lightning speed, dart sideways and backwards, rise vertically like a helicopter and accelerate rapidly from rest. Due to its outstanding flying ability a dragonfly can carry a weight which, in proportion to its own body-weight, far exceeds the pay-loads of aeroplanes or birds of prey. During fertilisation, for instance, the female carries her partner through the air, attached to the end of her body by two claws, thus carrying a weight equal to her own. An aeroplane cannot approach such a performance and a bird of prey can usually only carry a load of one-third its own body-weight. Even then the weight is carried in the talons, near the bird's centre of gravity, and not on the tail.

If we wander across the fields in late summer we may sometimes see tiny spiders floating through the air attached to fine threads. They are in search of new feeding grounds, and at the end of their journey they pull in the thread, like a seaman reefing sail, and sink gently to the ground.

An even more unusual method of making use of the air has been developed by the water spider, *Argyroneta*. Observing one of these animals in calm water, one sees them diving gracefully and spinning a horizontal net between the stems of water plants. When the net is completed, the spider carries minute bubbles of air downwards and releases them below the net which swells like a balloon. When the job is finished the spider has a tent of air below the water in which it can rear its young, undisturbed by its enemies on land.

Species from nearly all types of vertebrate have made the air their habitat. The flying fish of the tropical Atlantic ocean can jump from the sea after a short underwater run, rise to a height of twenty feet and glide six hundred feet when wind conditions are favourable. There are flying frogs, squirrels and lizards which have special flying skins with which they can glide through the air for varying distances. These special areas of skin have evolved to enable these animals to escape their enemies and to help them find food. The greatest wing span, attained by the flying Saurians fifty million years ago, measured up to twenty-six feet.

The bats are the best flyers among the mammals, and they have completely adapted their flight for the capture of nocturnal insects. The wings of skin between the elongated bones of the hand enable them to change direction by ninety degrees with a single beat of the wing lasting less than one-twentieth of a second. Because of this agility even birds of prey cannot catch bats in flight.

The first feathered bird on earth, according to the zoologists was *Archeopteryx* from the Jurassic period. This curious creature was evolved from reptile-like ancestors about 140 million years ago. Its fossil still shows toothed jaws, clawed feet, and an extraordinarily long tail spine. On the other hand, *Archeopteryx* already had true feathers consisting of shafts and barbs and these enabled it to fly.

Since Jurassic times birds have developed an amazing variety of form; from the humming bird, weighing about one-fifteenth of an ounce, to the ostrich of about four hundred and forty pounds; from the diving penguin to the albatross, unsurpassed as a gliding artist. There are about ten thousand known species of birds, most of which live in the tropics. The small South American state of Ecuador harbours about one thousand, two hundred species, while England has less than two hundred nesting breeds, of which only about one hundred are common.

All the organs of birds are specially adapted for life in the air. If you have ever held a small bird in your hand you know what a "featherweight" it is. The reasons for this lightness are the numerous air spaces in the body, the air pockets in the chest and the hollow shaft bones.

In contrast to man, to whom the air is a light, mobile gas, for the bird the air resembles a fluid of very low density in which it has to swim. To do this it makes oar-like movements with its wings. In the course of this movement the weight is shifted rhythmically to the wing tips on the down beat, and to the part of the wing nearest the body on the up beat. This enables the body to remain on a level course through the air, instead of rising with the down stroke and falling with the up stroke.

Birds that do a lot of flying need an unusually large amount of food to compensate for their great expenditure of energy. A song-bird like the warbler, which feeds on the wing, eats nearly its own weight in insects daily. This is equivalent to a daily ration of about a thousand sausages for a man. To digest the food as rapidly as possible, these birds have extra strong stomach muscles which grind the food into small pieces. Hard though it is to believe, a turkey can easily grind twenty-four walnuts, shells and all, into a fine mash in twenty-four hours. The comparatively high body temperature of birds is also a help in the chemistry of digestion. Most birds have a temperature of 42-45 degrees Centigrade, which would be a fatal fever in man.

The performances in flight of some birds are quite astonishing. Ornithologists differentiate eight different types of progress through the air.

1. Sailing.
2. Gliding.
3. Waveflight.
4. Hovering (stationary flight).
5. Undulating or kite-like flight (pigeon).
6. Static sail flight in up currents (buzzard, gull).
7. Lifting and whirring (finch, hummingbird, kingfisher).
8. Dynamic sailflight (albatross).

The wing-beats of nectar-sucking humming-birds hovering in front of a flower have been measured as fifty to sixty per second. When the wind has a certain minimum velocity the albatross, with a wing span of more than twelve feet, can glide for days above the water without moving its wings. Rising against the wind or side-slipping, it develops the greatest refinement of gliding technique known to us, which no other bird can hope to emulate.

The "gliders" amongst the birds are helped by invisible columns of hot, rising air and by up-currents from hills, mountains and dunes. When the upward speed of the air is greater than the sailing speed of the bird, they can rise without moving a wing. This is the case with buzzards who spiral up on "thermals" to apparently limitless heights.

Desert vultures also know how to make good use of warm air currents, but the greatest experts are the gulls. They not only let themselves be carried across the sand dunes by up-draughts, but have also learned that there are rising air currents behind a ship which is steaming into the wind. They use these currents to follow the steamer effortlessly and, when the boat changes direction so that the wind blows diagonally across the bows, they change their position to the left or right behind the stern. A following wind, however, does not cause up-draughts. In such cases the passengers are disappointed and never, or rarely, see a gull, for to keep up with the ship the gulls would have to move their wings vigorously and this would rapidly tire them. Even such weak up-currents as those across waves are sufficient to enable some sea-birds to rise easily from the water. Gulls simply wait until a wave reaches them, let themselves be carried to the crest, spread their wings and sail away in level flight.

What is true of gliding birds is also true of the long distance fliers. They too are experts in exploiting air currents. The Japanese bekassine is probably unequalled among the passerines with its uninterrupted flight of three thousand miles (equivalent to an Atlantic crossing). Some tern also achieve impressive performances when they cross twice yearly from one polar zone to the other, a distance of at least ten thousand miles, with only short stops on the way.

The flight speed of some birds is amazing. No bird can compete with a modern aeroplane, but the sprinters among the birds are still very fast. A carrier pigeon can reach 56 feet a second in windstill conditions and a mallard duck nearly 100. The American needle-tailed swift even reaches 130 feet a second, equivalent to 90 miles an hour. According to observers the African Pallas's sungrouse is the fastest bird on earth. Its speed has not yet been recorded but the narrow, pointed wings, tremendous muscles and mobile tail indicate incredible performances.

7

SOUND

No SOUNDS WOULD BE AUDIBLE without the air. All creatures except those living under water would be deaf without it, for it carries all sounds from their source to our ears and is a prerequisite of our sense of hearing. Sounds of all types are caused by vibrating bodies which rhythmically compress the air particles around them. A series of waves of dense and rarefied air is created which spreads outward in all directions. This simple fact is the basic secret of sound, and once you grasp it, its many various and often surprising manifestations are easy to understand.

A body causing such air waves must vibrate at least sixteen times a second before a sound can be heard. This would make a very deep note, the deepest our ears could perceive. The quicker the sound vibrations follow each other, the higher the note. This does not extend indefinitely, however, for the highest audible note is caused by a body which vibrates twenty thousand times a second; the physicist calls this a "frequency" of twenty thousand "Hertz." Higher rates of vibration are inaudible. The whole range of sound lies between 16 and 20,000 Hertz. The famous International "A," which is created when a tuning fork vibrates 435 times a second, is of special importance, for our musical scale is based on it and musicians tune their instruments by it.

All frequencies below sixteen vibrations per second are called "infrasonic" sounds, and those above 20,000 "ultrasonic."

Ultrasonic sound has many uses, but can be dangerous in the hands of a novice. In correct doses it can increase the blood flow through the skin or destroy malignantly proliferating tissue. Above a certain strength it can kill small organisms. Industry uses ultrasonic vibrations to coagulate and precipitate dust and soot particles in the air, or to disperse fog, making the fine droplets coalesce and fall to the ground. It can be used to drill holes through tree trunks, to investigate objects for cracks or other damage, to test the strength of metallic components, to emulsify immiscible liquids, to sterilise surgical instruments—technicians are constantly discovering new uses for this silent, invisible tool.

Some animals are superior to man in their ability to hear ultrasonic vibrations. Bats use them in an extraordinary manner to orientate themselves during flight. Their oddly-shaped larynx emits ultrasonic cries with a frequency of 30,000–80,000 Hertz. These act as a sort of radar, for their echo is reflected from any object, such as a tree, wall, wire or even a small insect, and returns to the bat's ears. Some bats can judge the ultrasonic echo so cleverly that they cannot only find their way quickly and safely at night, but can even differentiate whether the echo has been reflected from stone, wood, leaves or soft soil.

The perfection with which bats use the ultrasonic vibrations has no equal in the animal kingdom, but they are not the only creature who can hear them. Dogs also have this ability. If you own a dog you can amuse yourself by buying one of those inaudible ultrasonic dog whistles and "calling your dog to heel silently" over fairly long distances.

The sounds that reach us can be divided into notes, noises and detonations. Physicists classify them according to their origin. Notes are produced by completely even vibrations, noises by irregular ones and a detonation by a single violent air compression.

The air which has been set in vibration by a sound wave behaves like the bellows of an accordion. It is compressed to a variable degree, depending on the strength of vibration of the source. This strength in turn determines the loudness. Loudness is measured in "phons" and police officers sometimes use complicated machines to measure the phons given off by a stuttering motor-scooter or roaring motor-bicycle from which the owner has removed the silencer. Organisers of competitions use similar instruments to measure the applause of an audience when determining contest winners. During such contests the volume of applause can exceed the roar of traffic, but the phon-scale is wide enough to cope with sounds of any strength. It embraces the complete range, from the inaudible to the physically painful. For example:

Leaves gently rustling	10	Phon.
Whispers	20	"
Soft speech	40	"
Loud speech	60	"
Loud street noises	70	"
Shouting	80	"
Very loud motor horn	90	"
Maximum motor-cycle noise	100	"
Riveting hammer	110	"
Aeroplane motors at 12 ft.	120	"
Physically painful noise	130	"

A characteristic property of our ears was taken into consideration when constructing the phon-scale. If the number of very soft sources of sound is increased, for instance, the increase is clearly felt, but if the number of loud sources is doubled the increase is not nearly so apparent. In other words, the loudness, or "volume," is not proportional to the source (objective intensity) but to its logarithm. This is the Weber-Fechner law. Consequently, ten sources of 15 phon each do not result in 150 phon but only in 15 + 10 = 25 phon, not even twice the amount of one of them. Or, if we wanted to halve the amount of noise from ten Klaxon horns of 90 phons each we could not do so by silencing five of them; even if we stopped nine horns the remaining noise would be only one-tenth less than that of all of them put together. Soft sounds behave differently. Ten sources of one phon each give 1 + 10 = 11 phon.

The speed with which sound moves through the air is an important scientific fact. Once it is known it can be used to measure distances, and many difficult physical formulæ can be solved. Isaac Newton was the first physicist who seriously considered the velocity of sound. He conducted the first experiments in 1686, by measuring the time interval between the appearance of the flame from a distant cannon and the arrival of the report. A simple calculation based on the number of seconds and the distance of the cannon gave him the velocity. Newton's experiments were well thought out, but it was discovered later that his value was incorrect. The error was explained 130 years later, when the French astronomer Laplace showed that Newton had not taken into account the temperature of the air. It is a fact that temperature influences the velocity to a great extent and that hot air conducts sound better than cold air. The accepted modern value of 1088 feet per second always refers to 0° C. at sea-level.

There are many historic examples of sound waves travelling long distances, the most famous of which is undoubtedly the detonation from the eruption of the volcano Krakatoa in 1883, which shook the earth like an elemental thunderbolt. The sound waves were audible over one-thirteenth of the whole globe. It could be heard about three thousand miles away on the island of Madagascar, and presumably there have never been so many burst eardrums in the neighbourhood of any other volcano.

As it moves through space, a sound wave behaves similarly to a light wave. It can be reflected, deflected or bent. A smooth wall, for instance, is enough to send a sound back to its source. Echoes are created in this manner. In answer to the question: "Where are little boys beaten?" for instance, an echo will promptly reply: "Eton." To the inquiry: "Who likes cider?" it answers: "Ida."

The complexities an echo can attain are demonstrated by a peculiar phenomenon near the town of Thale in the Harz mountains. A torrent flows between the "Rosstrappe" (Horse trap) and the "Hexentanzplatz" (Witches' Dance Floor), two masses of rock in the foothills. The steep cliffs form such curious angles that the bang of an explosion is tossed repeatedly from one rock face to another before dying away. An old man used once to make it his business and pleasure to demonstrate the "twelve-fold Rosstrappen echo" to tourists. He would fire an old-fashioned ball-loaded pistol down the valley. A thunderous reverberation followed, to which the listeners attended in breathless silence as it bounced like a ball from cliff to cliff until it faded into the distance.

Apart from quiet surroundings and still air (wind carries the sound away), a sufficient distance between the source and the reflecting surface is essential for an echo. If the distance is too short the echo returns too quickly and merely extends the caller's voice slightly. In the example given previously it would only reply "da" instead of "Ida." In large halls and churches this leads to unpleasant reverberations, which are sometimes deliberately imitated by radio technicians to give the impression of large rooms. The opposite effect occurs on mountains, the sea or in an open field, where there is practically no reverberation. In such surroundings the voice sounds toneless and empty because the colouring of a faint echo is missing.

Curved walls act on sound in a strange but not inexplicable way. Let us imagine a room with a concave wall. If a man stood at the focus of the curvature his reflected words would be bundled into a beam rather like the light from the headlamp of a car. If there were two such walls opposite each other, the second one would concentrate the sound, like a concave mirror, to a point in front of itself. Two people, each standing at a focal point, could then carry on a whispered conversation without being overheard by a third person in the same room. Their almost inaudible whispers

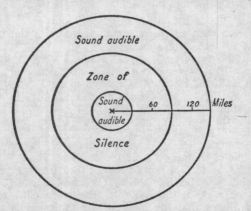

The "zone of silence" usually forms a ring round the source of sound.

would only be magnified at the focal points. Such rooms are called "whispering galleries" and if you want a demonstration, you can go to St. Paul's Cathedral in London, the Observatory in Paris or the Ratskeller in Bremen.

It seems odd that a sound can sometimes be heard at its source and vanish at a distance, only to be heard again still farther away. For a long time this "zone of silence" defeated all attempts at its explanation. At length a meteorologist discovered that layers of air of different temperature interfere with sound. Since the air immediately above the ground is usually warmer than that in higher layers the sound waves are deflected diagonally upwards, rather like the light waves of a mirage. The consequences are easily deduced. A certain distance from the source a sound becomes inaudible because it passes over our heads. At a height of about twenty-five miles, however, there is usually another layer of warm air and this deflects the sound back towards the earth. This explains why there is a region of audibility beyond the zone of silence. A typical example was the Moscow explosion of 1920, the detonation of which could be heard clearly for about thirty miles. Then it disappeared, only to reappear again at a distance of about ninety miles from the centre of the explosion, remaining audible for another sixty miles or so. In rare cases the warm air above the earth can reflect the sound upwards once more and cause a second or even third zone of silence. In cross section you can see the track of the sound-wave curving like a giant snake above the earth.

An equally strange phenomenon occurs when a source of sound moves rapidly towards an observer. You must have heard examples of this. Why, for instance, does the note of an approaching railway engine rise? It is due to the "Doppler effect" (named after the Austrian mathematician Doppler), and it is caused by compression of the sound-waves from the approaching source, just as they are pulled farther apart when the source is receding. We already know that increasing frequency causes a rise in pitch, so that in one case the note will rise up the scale and in the other it will fall.

We have now mentioned all the most important manifestations of sound, but we have not yet described the ear, the sensitive and delicately constructed organ which receives them.

The sound-waves first of all meet the shell of the ear. This conducts them along a narrow channel, the thickness of your

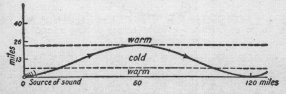

Cross section: the course of a sound wave in the atmosphere, causing a "zone of silence."

little finger, to the eardrum. This passage is filled with fine
hairs, arranged as in a lobster pot, which catch small foreign
bodies and insects and prevent them from reaching the ear-
drum but do not interfere with the sound-waves. The ear-
drum itself is a fine membrane stretched diagonally across
the end of the passage. It is pulled inwards at the centre to
assume a funnel shape and transmits the sound vibration
to three curiously shaped bones in the middle ear. These are
the malleus, incus and stapes (hammer, anvil and stirrup),
the tiny ossicles of hearing and the smallest bones in our
body. The last of them, the stirrup, has the task of transfer-
ring the sound waves to an oval window (fenestra ovalis)
which in turn transmits them, via the hearing fluid (perilymph), to the organ of hearing proper. This organ is the
"cochlea" and its convolutions contain up to 24,000 very
fine fibres of all lengths, stretched like the strings of a piano
and running in all directions. As the sound waves pass
through the perilymph they set some of these fibres in motion, according to the pitch of the original note. The vibrating fibres stimulate the auditory nerves and these lead to the
perception of sound in the centre of hearing in the brain.

The ear is an astonishing organ. It is debatable which is
the more remarkable, the ability to differentiate between
fine nuances of pitch, or the ability to find where a sound
comes from without the help of sight. If you have ever been
in a dark room with a ticking clock you realise how easy
it is to locate it by your sense of hearing alone. We believe
that we know how the ear accomplishes this feat. If a sound
does not come from directly in front of us the waves will
reach one ear a fraction of a second earlier than the other.
Tests have shown that our ears can detect the infinitesimal
time interval of 0.00003 seconds and use it to find out
where a sound comes from.

8

THE ATMOSPHERE OF OTHER PLANETS

GAZING AT THE SKY THROUGH A TELESCOPE, the stars, planets
and particularly the moon with its craters and shadows seem
as sharply defined as if hewn in stone. Yet despite this apparent clarity we in fact see the heavenly bodies through an
imperfect pane of glass.

This pane of glass is our atmosphere. Spread invisibly

above the earth, a mere exhalation, it is yet dense enough sometimes to drive astronomers to despair. Let us take an example; the chemical elements contained in the atmosphere of a star can be determined by investigation of the light from that star. Before reaching our telescopes, however, the light must travel through the atmosphere, which swallows up part of it. The atmosphere may also mislead observers by showing them elements contained by itself which are not present on the star. For this reason astronomers would much prefer to build their telescopes on the moon, where there is no interfering atmosphere to cause "twinkling" and distort their pictures. The latest researches make it probable, however, that the moon also is surrounded by a layer of gas a fraction of an inch thick.

But let us not be too critical of our atmosphere, for our solar system contains planets, Venus for instance, whose inhabitants, if there were any, could never see the sky at all because of unbroken thick clouds.

Besides such "masked" planets, there are some bodies in space which have no protective covering of air at all. They are exposed to all the dangers from outer space. A hail of meteors of all sizes bombards them, for there is no gas or atmosphere to burn away these "bullets from outer space" by friction, converting them into shooting stars at a safe height. On the contrary, the skies of such stars threaten them with mortal danger. Deadly ultra-violet rays and cosmic rays burn down on them. The sun and the stars blaze like white flames in a sky of inky blackness. No winds sweep across them, no colour relieves their monotony, no sound disturbs their desolation, for even the impact of a meteor would be inaudible, since sound needs air before it can reach the ear of a living creature.

Planets which possess an atmosphere are in a different position. They are not exposed to rays from outer space; they can develop beneath the protection of the enveloping air, and where conditions are right life can emerge.

Let us imagine our solar system on a scale many thousand million times smaller. The sun would be a glowing ball of gas about four and a half feet in diameter. Mercury, the planet nearest the sun, would be pea-sized and have an orbit of 190 feet. Venus would be the size of a cherry, at a distance of 350 feet. Then follows the earth, also cherry-sized, at 490 feet; Jupiter the size of a coconut at 2500 feet; Saturn also coconut-sized at almost a mile; apple-sized Uranus at 1¾ miles; apple-sized Neptune 2¾ miles away and finally Pluto, an escaped moon of Neptune, pea-sized at a distance of 3¾ miles.

What are these planets like, and what do we know about their atmospheres?

Astronomers have found only faint traces of an atmosphere on Mercury. It is difficult to observe because of its proximity to the sun's overpowering light. Mercury may once in fact have possessed more of an atmosphere. Since it in all probability always presents the same face to the sun, that side must be very hot, presumably 400° C. The night-side, on the other hand, is very cold, about −100° C. Under such conditions the gases of an atmosphere, especially the heavy ones, may migrate from the hot to the cold side and accumulate there. Perhaps the low temperatures on the night-side have even led to liquification or solidification of the gases. We are not sure whether such a process has taken place, but it is quite possible.

On Venus, the morning or evening star, the conditions are quite different. Next to the sun and moon, Venus is the brightest body in the sky and we know the secret of its brightness. It has a comparatively dense atmosphere, about forty miles deep, which refracts and scatters the sunlight more strongly than our own. It is not, however, the completely impenetrable cloud layer that it was once believed to be. We can see through the cloud to the surface of the planet. On photographs taken with ultra-violet light the astronomer Kniper found indications of curious, belt-like bands surrounding the planet. These bands could not be explained, but from their position and movement Kniper deduced that Venus rotates round a tilted axis similar to our own.

J. D. Kraus, of Ohio State University, reached a similar conclusion from radio-astronomic observations. Between the spring and autumn of 1956, Kraus received eleven metre bands of irregular strength which indicated thunderstorm activity on Venus. Taking the strength of these waves and earth's rotation into consideration, he established a daily curve which showed a maximum every twenty-two hours and seventeen minutes. It is possible that a certain spot on Venus acts as a "transmitter" and that these maxima coincide with the time of rotation, which according to Kraus's experiments would be nearly the same as our own.

What about living organisms on Venus? Spectrum analysis has shown the presence of carbon dioxide in the atmosphere of Venus, but water vapour and the essential oxygen are absent. The thunderstorm activity suggests that the upper atmospheric layers are very cold, while those near the surface are at least 100° C., for only under such conditions could thunderstorms occur. This invalidates the previous belief in swampy, primeval forests. Life as we know it is dependent, among other things, on water and proteins. Both these essentials are impossible on Venus; at such high surface temperatures water would evaporate and albumen coagulate.

Mars has much more in common with the earth. It is called the red planet, but its reddish glow is due to its atmosphere and not to its surface. In the autumn of 1956 Mars was closer to the earth than at any time since 1924, and astronomers had a good opportunity to observe it. On the 10th of September of that year it was "in opposition" to the sun. This means that the earth, which has a smaller orbit around the sun, caught up with Mars rather like the inside runner on the bends during a staggered race. The two planets and the sun stood in a straight line, the sun on the day-side of the earth and Mars on the night-side.

While observing Mars for 130 nights in the summer and autumn of 1956, the American Mars specialist, Slipher, took thousands of photographs from the Lamont-Hussey observatory in South Africa. He sometimes worked with electronic optical enlargers which cast a two-inch picture of the planet on his screen. Astronomers from all countries concentrated on Mars. Working in the Alma Ata observatory in Kasakstan, the Russian scientist Tikhow declared that his observations showed the white spots on the Martian poles to be layers of frozen water a few inches thick. These "polar caps" left so much water behind them when they melted in spring that the soil near them got soaked and took on a reddish-brown colour, probably due to primitive plants which grew there. Simultaneously with the thaw, the atmosphere carried a wave of moisture from the polar cap towards the equator at a daily rate of about thirty miles.

W. H. Wright was the first scientist to prove the presence of an atmosphere round Mars by photography. In 1924 he photographed Mars using an optical filter transmitting only ultra-violet rays, followed by a photograph using a red filter. The second photograph showed clearly the details on the planet's surface while the first one did not. The explanation could only be that there is a sort of barrier for ultra-violet rays in the air on Mars. Only the red rays penetrate to the surface and give rise to the planet's red appearance.

Later observers, including Slipher, confirmed these results and discovered another curious fact. The atmosphere on Mars is not always impenetrable to ultra-violet rays; sometimes it falls apart like a stage curtain. On such occasions ultra-violet photographs show the outline of small pieces of Martian landscape. The American astronomer Kniper believes the barrier zone to be a veil of cloud which is not always completely closed, and which is composed of ice crystals each measuring about 0.0001 of an inch.

There are other enigmas in the Martian atmosphere besides the curious clouds which can only be seen on ultra-violet photographs, such as two other types of cloud which are visible on red filter photographs. The first type are the so-called "yellow" clouds which probably consist of whirled up dust. Their movement shows that winds of up to sixty miles per hour occur on the planet. The second type are the "white" clouds, presumably veils of ice crystals. They are particularly clearly visible when Mars is farthest away from the sun on its elliptical orbit, that is when the surface is coldest and most favourable to ice formation.

Martian clouds usually disperse in the morning and re-form towards evening, but there are certain exceptions. In 1954, for instance, observers saw a W-shaped cloud over one particular spot on the surface, where it remained for most of one afternoon. This unusual occurrence is still to be explained.

Taken as a whole, the atmosphere on Mars is very thin compared to our own. Its density at surface level is equivalent to that above our highest mountains, and a man would suffocate in it after three minutes. Its estimated height is about sixty miles, and it exerts a pressure of about eighty millibars on the surface, only about one-tenth of ours at sea-level. If we wanted to compare the Martian landscape with our own, we would have to take the arid rock deserts of Tibet and imagine the air to be even thinner than that above Mount Everest.

As Earth and Mars are both planets of the sun and have certain other similarities (length of day, inclined axis, cooled surface), they share certain atmospheric properties. The air on Mars also has high and low pressure areas around which the wind circulates. Because of Mars' rotation these areas move across the surface from West to East, just as on Earth. We can also assume that there is a low pressure belt along the Martian equator, but since it contains little water vapour, the Martian atmosphere does not show its low pressure areas by typical, heavy cloud formations the way ours does.

The presence of distinct seasons on a planet depends on the inclination of its rotational axis to the plane of its orbit round the sun, as well as on the time of rotation round the sun (length of year) and on its atmosphere. The angle of the Martian axis is 25 degrees, very similar to our own (23.5 degrees), but the Martian year is 687 days. The atmosphere on Mars is thinner than ours and of different composition. It contains, as far as we know to-day, 98.5 per cent nitrogen and 0.25 per cent carbon dioxide, the remainder probably being the inert gas, argon.

Astronomers have calculated the length of the seasons on Mars to be as follows: the southern hemisphere has a spring of 145.6 days, summer 160.1, autumn 199.6 and winter 181.7 days. In the northern hemisphere the values of the seasons are reversed. The climatic difference between the two must, therefore, be considerable. One-half has a short summer, which is warm because of the proximity of the sun, and a long winter. The other has a short winter and a long, but only moderately warm summer.

Because of its low density the Martian atmosphere does not have the "hot-house" action of our own, and the difference between night and day must be greater than on the earth. On the Martian equator the temperature rises to 25° C. at noon but falls to −75° C. at night. In the polar regions of either hemisphere it remains well below freezing point day and night.

Since Mars only possesses one-tenth of earth's mass its gravitational force is much weaker. On Mars elephants could leap as lightly as gazelles. The lower gravity also means that the atmosphere is not as firmly held as ours. Many scientists believe that the lighter gases such as hydrogen and helium therefore escaped from the Martian atmosphere at an early date. Only the heavier gases remained behind and they constitute its present atmosphere.

It has not yet been possible to prove the presence of oxygen in the Martian atmosphere with any certainty. There is still a possibility, however, that small amounts of oxygen, perhaps between a thousandth and a hundredth of our own, do exist. Unless we suppose that the primitive Martian plants could obtain their essential oxygen from the soil (where according to the astro-physicist H. N. Russell it exists in bound form) by chemical reactions, they would have to get their oxygen from the dwindling amount in the atmosphere by a method unknown to us. Higher organisms which are more immediately dependent on oxygen could not survive in any case, as far as we can judge, because of the extreme climate. The higher water-containing plants, for instance, could not exist in the very low temperatures of the Martian night, they would simply freeze to death. Apart from all this there is the fact that the average yearly temperature on Mars is at least thirty degrees centigrade lower than ours. If our thermometer were to fall as low as that, the consequences would be disastrous; we have only to consider that a fall of 4 to 6° C. in the average temperature would produce a new ice-age.

Jupiter is a mysterious planet, and the most mysterious thing about it is perhaps the pink or salmon-coloured spot which drifts across its striated surface. Is it a mass of clouds? Is it a formation on the surface? We do not know.

Jupiter is much smaller than the sun but, because of its immense mass, its gravitation is so powerful that a man would be held to the surface like a bit of iron to a magnet. If the inhabitants of Jupiter had human muscles and were still to retain the same mobility as animals on earth, they could only grow about one foot high. The atmosphere on Jupiter is also subject to this strong gravitation, so that even the light, mobile gases cannot escape into space, and it is, therefore, not surprising that the air contains large amounts of hydrogen.

That there is life on Jupiter is extremely improbable since its air is poisonous to living organisms as we know them. The atmosphere extends to a great height, is very dense and consists of marsh gas (methane), ammonia and presumably large amounts of hydrogen. Moreover, in this stuffy dampness thunderstorms of such violence rage, that compared to them our own are in all probability harmless pyrotechnics. The radio waves created by these discharges can with directional antennæ be received on earth. These atmospheric thunderstorms suggest that on Jupiter, just as on Venus, the temperature rises markedly between the upper layers of the air and the surface, which is probably very warm, if not hot. There must be at least one point on Jupiter which continuously radiates strong heat. But where is this point? Is it connected with the mysterious pink mark? How is the heat generated? As with so many of the problems of nature we can only shrug our shoulders and guess. With Jupiter, however, there remains the hope that its secrets will be revealed by future investigation with radio-astronomy.

Atmospheric conditions similar to those on Jupiter exist on Uranus, the only planet which does not spin like a top from West to East, but instead revolves like a wheel around an almost horizontal axis. On Uranus also life as we know it is improbable. The study of reflected sunlight has demonstrated to astronomers that the atmosphere consists mainly of methane and ammonia. If the measurements of thermoelements coupled to telescopes are correct, the temperature on Uranus is about −200° C. A similar picture is shown by Neptune and Saturn. Methane, ammonia and also presumably large amounts of hydrogen characterise the atmospheres of all the large planets.

Our solar system has nine planets—Pluto with its frozen atmosphere is the ninth—but only the earth, and probably

Mars, possess living organisms. But the universe is large and includes endless numbers of suns and planets. In the Milky Way alone the number of suns is estimated at a hundred million and in the Universe it must run into billions. Even if all of these suns do not have planets, some of them do. It would be against all the laws of probability that the Earth and Mars should be the only ones to possess life, and that no other planet in the universe had an atmosphere with a development similar to our own which provided the prerequisites for the creation of life; that of Venus, for instance, is at a stage similar to the primordial atmosphere of the earth. The "curious coincidence" to which the creation of life was once attributed no longer has sufficient authority to be taken seriously.

9

THE FATE OF THE ATMOSPHERE

LET US LEAVE SPACE and return to the earth with its atmosphere of nitrogen, oxygen, carbon dioxide and rare gases which nourish life and millions of plants, animals and humans. Let us see if we can predict the future of our atmosphere and its final fate. We must realise that such conjectures are only hypotheses: suppositions based on "the best knowledge and conscience" of modern scientific understanding, but suffering from the drawbacks of all such suppositions in that they do not offer facts and have not been established.

In terms of a human, or even a historic time span our atmosphere appears unchanged. Pre-historic man certainly breathed the same air as we and equally certainly men 100,-000 years after us will also do so, if the composition of the air has not been changed artificially.

If, however, we consider the natural fate of the air over a longer period, such as several million years, the picture changes. What will inevitably happen is the exact opposite: gradual change and the disappearance of carbon dioxide. The volcanoes and gas sources in the earth, which are the main producers of carbon dioxide, are not inexhaustible. With the gradual subsidence of the earth's crust their activity will decrease, and they will generate less carbon dioxide. The plants, which combine this gas with water in the presence of light to form sugar and oxygen, will very gradually but inevitably lose a vital element. Experiments under glass show, beyond doubt, that certain plants already suffer from a slight carbon dioxide starvation. They grow much better in a hot-house atmosphere slightly enriched with carbon dioxide.

What will happen when the earth's supplies of carbon dioxide cease? The consequences are clear. At first the plants will be forced to consume the existing store and finally take up the carbon dioxide in the air, like an animal licking up the last drops of water from a well which has run dry. After that all the men and animals on earth whose existence is dependent on plant life will, sooner or later, face the same fate. There could be only one way out of this predicament. New forms of life would have to develop capable of coping with the altered atmospheric conditions. Unless this occurred all forms of life, with perhaps the exception of a few very primitive types, would die out.

Even if life adapted itself to the disappearance of carbon dioxide there would still come a day, far in the future, when it would be doomed down to the last alga and bacterium.

We can say that none of our immediate descendants will see this day for it lies in the far distant future. If we assume that the earth is not destroyed by an unexpected cosmic catastrophe and continues revolving round the sun in its usual manner, there are, as far as is known, two possible ways in which the destruction of the atmosphere and of life on earth could come about.

The first and less probable is death by cold. This would originate in the sun. It is known that the sun loses in weight while radiating heat and light, and it has been calculated that the loss amounts to about four million tons a second. The sun is so enormously large that this loss is negligible at present, but, over a long time, it must affect the amount of heat and light radiation, if (and this is the contested point of this theory) other chemico-physical processes do not provide compensation. Let us assume, however, that there is no such compensation and that the sun's energy is lessened by a continual loss in mass. This would lead to a gradual lowering of our temperature. Apart from this, the attractive force exerted by the sun on the earth would decrease, for it depends on mass. The consequences of this can easily be shown by a comparison. Let us imagine the sun's attractive force to be a rubber band to which the earth is fastened and by which it is whirled around like an athlete's hammer. What happens when the elastic strength of the rubber decreases? Due to its centrifugal force the earth would describe an ever widening arc around the sun and recede progressively from its already diminishing supply of light and heat. The seasons would grow colder and colder until the thermometer would not rise above freezing point even in July. Rivers, lakes and seas would be frozen solid. In the atmosphere, the ozone layer which protects us from the dangerous ultra-violet rays and which owes its existence to the sun, would become thinner and thinner. Increasing cold would markedly affect the composition of the air. Oxygen would disappear since its source, the sun-seeking plants, would die out. The circulation of the great planetary winds would cease, for the sun's heat would no longer suffice to keep them in motion. Finally nothing would be left of our air but a desolate, poisonous emanation in which no living creature could exist. Even this atmosphere would probably solidify on further cooling. This theory is controversial, however, as we said before. In the opinion of many scientists a different event would take place before death by cold overtook us—the destruction of this planet by fire. If we try to imagine this process we obtain a picture similar to that in the Revelation of St. John, xvi, 8, "And the fourth angel poured out his vial upon the sun; and power was given unto him to scorch men with fire."

We know that the mighty atomic furnace of the inner sun, working at a temperature of ten to fifteen million degrees centigrade, continuously converts hydrogen into helium and liberates 200,000 kilowatt hours of energy for every gramme of helium formed. This process will continue for many millions of years, for the sun still has a sufficient store of "fuel." After five or ten thousand million years, however, there will be a development in the centre of the sun which will finally burn away the air and incinerate the earth. This melodramatic finale of all life will be started by a lack of hydrogen in the sun's core. The energy given by the inner sun to the outer layers will grow less and less. The atomic furnace of the core will spread outwards like a grass fire on a windless day. Many scientists believe that this will not cause the sun to grow darker but—however paradoxical this may seem—make it grow brighter and brighter. It will expand into a gigantic red star composed of extremely finely dispersed matter with a flaming gaseous covering, extending as far as the present orbit of Mercury. In the long run this increase in heat would make life on earth unbearable. It has been calculated that when the sun has used up only one-third of its present store of hydrogen no living creature could exist on earth, even at the poles, and that the atmosphere, set into violent motion by the heat, would gradually escape into space.

The fiery death of our planet could also occur suddenly.

Year after year astronomers have noticed suns in the Milky Way suddenly flare up with an extraordinary brightness. The origin of this curious phenomenon, or "nova-eruption," has not been fully explained. The waves of heat and light generated by such an eruption border on the inconceivable. The luminosity of the sun would instantaneously increase ten thousand fold, and the earth would behold a natural spectacle of unsurpassed horror.

Since light from the sun takes about eight minutes to reach us, the heat wave from such a catastrophe would require about the same time to reach the day-side of the earth. After that short period of grace the first thing it met would be the atmosphere, which would literally burn away and char all life to a cinder. The air on the night-side of the globe would rush into the vacuum thus created in the greatest storm ever witnessed on earth. The winds would strip the surface bare, whirling away everything in their path and leaving only dead matter behind.

The heat would melt the polar ice and vaporise lakes, rivers and seas, and cause the hills and plains to glow. For a short time the atmosphere would be filled with hot bubbling vapours as it was once before, many thousand million years ago when the earth was new. Finally the vapours would escape into space and the earth would be left behind as a charred, shapeless lump in the Universe.

The sun would not be dead, however. When its glowing breath had expired it would be colder than before, but it would still be shining. Millions of years would pass in which the earth could cool down once more, and possibly re-form a primitive atmosphere. Perhaps this atmosphere might even reproduce the conditions necessary for the origin of life, but the fate of the earth would be sealed anyway. After the first eruption of the sun a second would inevitably follow, and after that a third and more. Each time a fatal heat shock would hit the earth, and each time the earth would become incandescent like a glowing ember. Many astronomers believe that the sun will go on erupting until it has finally spent all its energy. After that the earth would drift about cold and lifeless in the infinity of space. No breath of wind would disturb its petrified continents.

Luckily that day still seems very far off. The earth still lives, with the atmosphere covering our green fields like a gentle, protecting veil.

10

WEATHER AND WEATHER FORECASTING

THE AIR HAS FOUR PROPERTIES without which no living organism could exist, and without which the higher forms of life on earth could not have evolved. These four properties are:

1. The presence of oxygen, the gas essential for life.
2. The power to protect the earth from excesses of heat and cold.
3. The ability to store moisture and carry it over long distances.
4. The capacity to ward off the deadly portion of the ultraviolet rays of the sun.

The beneficial action of the air has been taken for granted by men to such an extent that they hardly ever think about its causes. If only one small, insignificant cog in the machinery of nature were lost, however, the invisible element would kill us all.

Let us imagine that the air were to stop moving. What would happen? On that day the heat in the tropics would become unbearable, the higher latitudes would freeze. The circulation of the essential gases such as oxygen, nitrogen and carbon dioxide would cease, and large towns would suffocate in their own exhalations.

Luckily, the atmosphere is in constant motion. Winds and storms blow across the earth and transfer the heat of the tropics to the colder regions in the north and south. They carry water vapour from the air above the large oceans to inland areas, where it is deposited as rain, snow or dew, which replenish lakes and streams and refresh animals and plants. It is the moving air which fertilises wind-pollinated plants in spring and summer, and helps the trees to shed their withered leaves in autumn and, like a mighty bellows, cleanses industrial cities of dust and poisonous gases.

What explains the restlessness of the atmosphere? What causes it to move easily and apparently weightlessly in all directions?

We all know that the air is a gas. This means that its components do not cling to each other as firmly as those of a liquid, much less adhere as rigidly to each other as the molecules of a solid substance. They are free and mobile, and move more easily than billiard-balls.

The engine which keeps the air in motion is the sun. The warming rays fall on the ground, which reflects them and thus heats the atmosphere from below, like the hotplate of an oven. If you have ever seen the shimmering air above a hot road in summer, you know this process from your own experience. The shimmer is the visible sign that the sun's heat is being transferred from the ground to the layer of air nearest to it. These layers rise and make room for the cooler, heavier layers which sink down from above. An exchange is created which gradually involves ever higher layers of air. The weather expert calls this "heating by convection," a vertical air movement which plays an important part in the heat economy of nature.

Since the warmth of the sun sets the air in motion, it represents a source of energy. A calculation of this energy shows that the portion of rays penetrating to the soil (which is only a small part of the total) would in one year melt an one hundred feet thick armour of ice covering the whole earth. On their way through the air the rays lose a good deal of their energy (about half), but on the very edge of the atmosphere they possess their full power because they have not been stopped by the "braking power" of the aerial envelope. The power the solar rays exert on the atmosphere can be gauged by the fact that even the most violent storms would cease completely if the rays were absent for only twelve days.

All the many complex and seemingly random movements of the air are based on this one simple natural act, the warming of the earth's surface. If the sun were to shine only on one place, the air would rise continually from that spot and the heat would spread evenly in all directions. The sun, however, shines all over the earth, to a varying degree according to the time of day or year, and the earth is warmed to a different extent according to the composition of its surface. Land masses warm more rapidly than seas, rocks or deserts more rapidly than fields and pastures. Consequently the air grows hotter in some places than in others, becoming lighter or heavier according to the temperature and giving rise to differences in pressure which the winds try to even out.

The majority of local breezes and most winds and storms owe their existence to the sun. Even the wide-ranging "planetary wind system," which encompasses the whole globe, would be impossible without it. Generally speaking the air is warmest at the equator, where the sun stands high in the sky and generates most heat because its rays meet the earth vertically. In higher latitudes the rays fall diagonally and in the polar regions almost horizontally, so that they have to travel farther through the atmosphere.

Let us follow a parcel of this air as, warmed by the sun, it rises above the equator. What happens next? The following explanations and analogies are not too easy to understand and some readers may not wish to follow them. In that case they may safely skip the next few pages and carry on from page 80. However, I will try not to be too technical.

To return to our parcel of rising air. In the meantime it has reached a considerable height above the equator and is trying to flow towards one of the poles. Let us assume that its direction is northwards. If the earth were to stand still for a short while it would presumably set off exactly to the north, but, since the earth is unlikely to do so, the parcel is deflected from its dead northerly direction as if by an invisible hand.

To understand the cause of this deflection let us imagine that a giant is standing on the equator and that he wants to roll a medicine ball up the earth to the North Pole. Let us further imagine that he has painted the degree of latitude on which he is standing white, to help him keep his course straight. He propels the ball. What happens? Something most peculiar. The giant discovers to his astonishment that the ball has no intention of going to the North Pole. It leaves the straight line which he has carefully painted and almost at once shifts over to the right—eastwards.

To explain its curious behavior we must remember two laws of physics which affect it. One is inertia, a property which all bodies possess, and which is a resistance to any alteration in their motion. Let us explain this a little further. The ball is already moving before the giant throws it, and therefore possesses some inertia. You may ask why. Well, it is the movement which the earth itself has imparted to it. The ball, the giant, and all other things anywhere on the earth's surface (except at the poles) move around the axis of the earth. Objects on the equator move particularly fast (about 1500 feet a second) because they are farthest away from the axis—we will return to this point in a moment. The ball is, therefore, moving fairly rapidly from east to west while still in the giant's hand.

The second law states that a spot on the surface of the earth moves faster the nearer it gets to the equator. To understand this we need only imagine the horizontal rotating wheel in a fairground; the cautious people near the rim are thrown off almost at once while those near the hub (equivalent to the poles of the earth) do not move so quickly and can stay on much longer.

If we now imagine the earth cut into discs parallel to the equator we have a series of such rotating wheels of different sizes, small at the pole, larger in the middle latitudes and largest at the equator itself. It is easy to see that the rims of the smaller discs move more slowly than those of the larger ones, and that the equator moves fastest of all.

Our giant on the equator does not realise the speed at which he moves for, in contrast to the people on the wheel, he does not have to make an effort to stay put, as the gravitational pull of the earth is strong enough to anchor him down. In fact he only notices the east to west movement by the peculiar behaviour of the ball.

Why does the ball drift eastwards?

On its path it crosses lines which rotate with ever decreasing speed. In these circumstances the initially great east-to-west motion, which it possessed on the equator, comes into play and turns it more and more to the right until—at about the 35th degree of latitude—it seems to come directly from the west.

The same thing applies to the Southern Hemisphere. If the giant were to turn round on the equator and roll his ball towards the South Pole it would be deflected to the east as well (in this case to the left), because it would also cross consecutive lines of decreasing east-to-west motion.

Let us return to our parcel of air and compare it to the medicine ball. We now understand why it is deflected to the east long before it reaches the Pole or even the median latitudes; in other words it moves to the right in the Northern Hemisphere and to the left in the Southern.

By the time they reach the Horse Latitudes [1] thirty-five degrees south and north of the equator, the air streams which were originally directed towards the Poles move almost due east. They no longer move at the great height which they

[1] The name is said to come from the days of sail. Sailing ships with live horses on board were often becalmed in these zones and the animals reputed to have died for lack of food and water.

reached above the equator. Cooled by their passage, the wandering air masses have become heavier and sunk lower until they have finally reached the surface again. What happens to them now? Do they circle the earth gently in the horse latitudes? Does the air keep sinking down and pile up on the 35th degree of latitude?

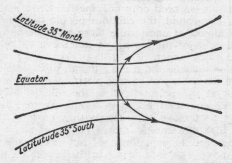

The deflecting power of the earth's rotation. A parcel of air rising above the equator and flowing towards the poles is deflected to the right in the Northern Hemisphere and to the left in the Southern.

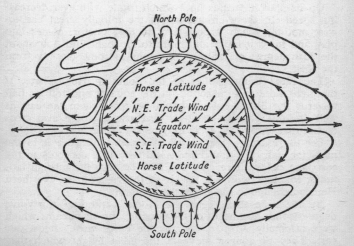

Diagrams of the earth's wind system with the prevailing wind directions in the trade wind, moderate and polar zones (after Bjerknes).

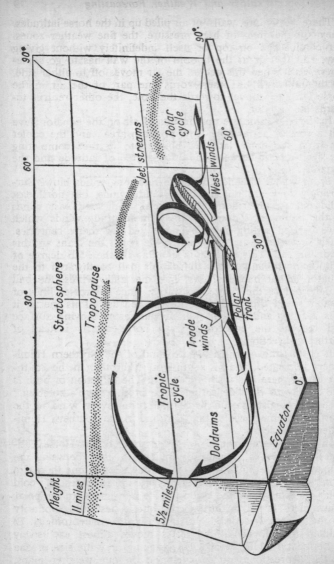

Circulation of air above the earth in winter, according to Palmén.

There really are walls of air piled up in the horse latitudes. They are the areas of high pressure, the fine weather zones. Air cannot pile on top of itself indefinitely without giving way, and the air at the bottom of the wall has to go somewhere else. When this occurs the air moves off to either side, north and south; in other words one part of the air in the horse latitudes moves towards the Pole, the other returns towards the equator.

In the meantime the up-currents of air on the equator have left a sort of aerial hole (low pressure area) and the cooler air from the horse latitudes blows into it, thus completing the cycle of air between the 35th degree of latitude and the equator.

From which direction do these returning winds blow? Surprisingly they are not north or south winds, but north-east winds in the Northern Hemisphere, and south-east winds in the Southern. These are the famous trade winds which have carried sailing ships over the sea for many centuries. Their secret is easily explained if we recall the giant and his medicine ball. This time he is standing on the 35th degree of latitude north and wants to roll his ball southwards to the equator. What happens? Just like the trade winds, the ball is deflected to the right, westwards, since it crosses lines of greater speed the farther it moves. Because of its inertia it falls farther and farther behind the faster moving surface and reaches the equator from a north-easterly instead of northerly direction.

It is thus the north-east trade wind of the Northern Hemisphere is created, and his south-easterly brother in the Southern Hemisphere has a similar origin. The direction of both is due simply to the "deflecting force of the earth's rotation," as meteorologists say, a force that turns every wind in the Northern Hemisphere to the right and in the Southern Hemisphere to the left.

In the temperate zones north and south of the Horse Latitudes a cycle is developed similar to that between the equator and the 35th degree of latitude. Conditions there are more unpredictable, however, as rapid advances of cold polar air often upset the system of air movement. In the polar zones there is yet a third cycle, but it has little similarity to the others. According to the Finnish meteorologist E. Palmén the air above the Poles moves almost exclusively in horizontal eddies, each eddy reaching only the size of one of the depressions, or anticyclones, on our weather maps.

If the sun is the engine and the earth's rotation the steering-wheel, the wandering high and low pressure areas are the sparking plugs of the changeable weather in our temperate latitudes. The German meteorologist Rodewald once compared the low pressure areas to actors and the high pressure areas to directors on the weather stage.

Before we can get any further we have to find out what high and low pressure areas are. Both concepts are closely connected with the weight of the air, which can be calculated by weighing a glass globe when it is full of air and when it is evacuated. The difference is the weight of the air, which is about 1.3 kilograms per cubic metre at sea-level (approximately one pound per 10 cubic feet of air).

But what is air pressure?

In 1643 the Italian Torricelli found the answer to this question by a famous experiment. He took a tube about one metre long and one square centimetre in cross section and sealed one end. After sucking out the air with a pump he closed the open end with his thumb and inverted it over a bowl of mercury so that the sealed end pointed vertically upwards. Then he removed his thumb. What happened? The mercury rose from the bowl into the evacuated tube. Higher and higher it went, until it reached a distance of about 760 millimetres above the level of the mercury in the bowl; there the ascent stopped.

Why, Torricelli wondered, did the mercury rise in the evacuated tube against all the laws of gravity? He was not satisfied with the explanation of his contemporaries which attributed such phenomena to the fact that, as the saying goes, "Nature abhors a vacuum." He decided that it had to be something explicable, something tangible and preferably something measurable, and so he finally hit upon the only fitting explanation. He told himself: "The weight of air which rests on everything on the earth must also exert a pressure on the mercury in the bowl. Nothing but the air pressure can have driven it into the glass tube, for there was no air in it and no resistance to overcome."

With his "760 millimetre column" Torricelli had found something with which to measure air pressure. He discovered that this pressure is simply the weight of the atmosphere. Expressed in different terms his experiment explained that the weight of a column of air one square centimetre in cross-section, reaching from sea-level to the upper edge of the atmosphere, equalled the weight of a column of mercury one square centimetre in cross section and 760 millimetres high (about 30 inches). Since a cubic centimetre of mercury weighs 13.6 grammes (about half an ounce) such a column weighs 1.03 kilograms (about 2¼ pounds). Let us, just for fun, calculate the weight of air an average man supports unconsciously all the time. With a head diameter of 17 centimetres (about 6½ inches) the surface area (πr^2) equals 227 square centimetres (about 35 square inches) which means that our heads support a weight equal to 227 of those mercury columns. This equals a weight of approximately 230 kilogrammes (or 500 pounds) and we can only marvel that we do not collapse under it.

With his primitive glass tube Torricelli had, without realising it, invented the first usable barometer. Even to-day many measurements of air pressure are carried out according to his principle. These barometers are simply sensitive air balances, but we no longer measure the pressure in "millimetres of mercury" but in "millibars," because it is inconvenient to measure a weight (air pressure) with a standard of length. A millibar is the pressure exerted by one gramme on a surface one centimetre square.[2]

If you travelled vertically upwards in a helicopter, carrying a barometer in your hand, you could watch the pointer falling as you rose higher and higher. The air pressure lessens as we rise, and the barometer "falls." This is not surprising for, as we ascend, the amount of air below us increases and the air above us weighs correspondingly less.

Even without rising above the surface the weight of the atmosphere over an observer will vary within certain limits. This variation is caused by changes in weather conditions, particularly alterations of air density, which in their turn are caused by differences in air temperatures. So we come back to the starting point; variations in air temperature cause changes of air pressure.

Where a great deal of warm air rises above the ground the column of air grows lighter, and we get an area of low pressure or simply a "Low." Where, on the other hand, cool air sinks down the air column becomes heavier and a high pressure area or "High" develops. It can happen that an area of high barometric pressure is observed where there is an ascending stream of hot air. This apparent contradiction, which occurs most frequently in summer, is caused by a particularly cold mass of air at a height between six and eighteen miles which presses down on the lower, warmer layers.

If we look at the daily weather charts we can see oddly curved lines, which are often in the shape of rough circles round a point. They are the so called "isobars"—lines con-

---

[2] Since a column of mercury of one square centimetre cross-section and three-quarters of a millimetre height weighs just one gramme, one millibar equals three-quarters of a millimetre of mercury. A barometric pressure of 750 millimetres of mercury is, therefore, equivalent to 1000 millibars.

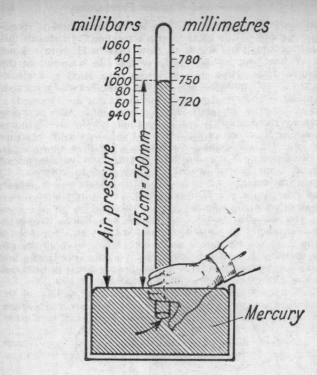

millibars   millimetres
1060
40
20   780
1000
80   750
60   720
940

Air pressure

75cm=750mm

Mercury

Torricelli's experiment.

necting points of equal air pressure. Their shape and the way
they change with time allows one to make correct deductions
about the development of the weather.

If the atmosphere were coloured, its restless movement to
and fro would be clearly visible. The Highs and Lows would
be seen as mountains and valleys of air, which sometimes
wander over the earth for long distances. We would observe
how they rise and fall, like cigarette smoke in a beam of sunlight.

Since the air, like all gases, can equalise differences of
pressure, a part of its mass flows out sideways from the high
pressure areas and streams into the low pressure ones. This
"law of the winds" was first perceived by the Dutch meteorologist Buys Ballot, who stated it in the form: "The wind
always blows from a region of higher pressure to a region
of lower pressure, and is turned to the right in the

Northern Hemisphere and to the left in the Southern Hemisphere by the power of the earth's rotation." In reality this deflection causes the winds to blow from a High to a Low, not in a straight line but more or less like a spiral. In the Northern Hemisphere they blow out of a High in a clockwise direction and into a Low in an anti-clockwise direction. In the Southern Hemisphere these directions are reversed.

The most important factors in the constantly changing interplay of the weather are vertical and horizontal air movements, changes in humidity, temperature, and pressure and the altering position of high and low pressure areas. These factors cause clouds, rain, winds, hail, thunderstorms and, not the least important, cloudless fine weather.

The many ways in which weather factors can combine, their co-operation or conflict and their almost endless interactions, are so complicated that generations of scientists have tried to bring order into this apparent chaos. Their attempts to find a formula which would solve all the problems of meteorological events in a simple manner have all been in vain. The atmosphere surrounds us like a huge organism and an event in one place can bring about a reaction in quite an-

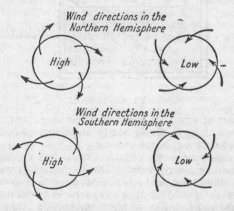

Wind directions in the Northern Hemisphere

High   Low

Wind directions in the Southern Hemisphere

High   Low

other, without our being able to foretell where or when. We can tell which processes in the air may cause rain or high jet-streams, for instance, and are even able to make limited forecasts with a reasonable amount of certainty, but it is impossible to predict each single weather factor and all its alterations, as well as the effect of these alterations on the atmosphere as a whole, so as to give an accurate picture of the coming weather for any one locality.

All these difficulties, which the expert recognises more clearly than the layman, have not prevented the development of strange notions about the weather and its causes. Numerous natural and even human phenomena have been ascribed to it. Many people still believe firmly in the "hundred year calendar," according to which a certain weather sequence will return every seven years. The baselessness of this superstition is demonstrated by the fact that the weather would have to conform to human time divisions, as if hens were expected to lay more eggs before public holidays so as to cover the increase of cakes baked during this period. This would be the more likely of the two, since hens at least have instincts. The last illusions about the hundred year calendar vanish when we investigate its origin. The threadbare idea behind it is based on observations made by Moritz Knauer, the Abbot of Bamberg, between 1652 and 1658. The observations themselves were probably quite reliable, although Knauer believed in astrology and always kept an eye on the planet that was in the ascendant. The Abbot recorded his observations in a calendar, and it is a copy of this which found its way into the hands of a business-like Doctor Hellwig of Thuringia around 1700. The doctor printed it after Knauer's death and falsely stated in the preface that the manuscript was a hundred years old. Apart from this he changed the past tense of the observations into the future, and in this manner gave a prophetic character to the unassuming records of the original. The damage was done. The readers interpreted Knauer's seven-year calendar as a recurring seven-year weather cycle. Many, misunderstanding this part, even believed that the weather of one particular day would recur every hundred years, hence the "hundred year calendar."

Equally unfounded is the belief about the moon's influence. "When the moon changes, the weather changes" you will hear people say. The basis of this error is easily explained. The weather in our latitudes is inconstant enough at the best of times, and rarely lasts more than four or five days without change. The chances of the moon theorists being correct are, therefore, considerable, especially as they usually leave themselves a few days leeway on either side of the lunar change.

How could the moon influence our weather? It has no effective radiation of its own (which amounts to only 1/100,000th of the sun's radiation) and the sunlight reflected by it is only 1/600,000th of the sun's own light. There remains the question of attraction. Can the moon attract the air in the same way that it attracts the sea to cause tides? Every physicist knows that the force by which two bodies attract each other is the product of their masses. The mass of the moon multiplied by the mass of the oceans gives a number large enough to explain the tides. The mass of the moon multiplied by the mass of the air does not give a large enough result to cause noticeable atmospheric tides. If they did occur they would show on our barometers, and we know that this is not the case.

The belief that the weather on a Sunday will be the same as that of the preceding Friday is equally nonsensical. The meteorologist Kassner investigated the saying that "As Friday ends, so Sunday will begin," and found that during nine years this was true in 278 cases and false in 243 cases, a ratio of 53 : 47 which could apply equally well for any random pair of days. The proverb arose from the wish to be able to predict the weather on the one day of the week when people look forward to going out.

The "seven sleepers" rule of Central Europe, that rain on the 27th of June will be followed by seven weeks rain (similar to the St. Swithin's legend in England), has a certain basis of fact. In that region rain at such a date is usually a sign that humid monsoon weather has arrived. Because of its geographical position wet summers are common in Central Europe. The hinterland of the large mass of Europe and Asia is heated by the sun in summer and develops a large low pressure region into which the cooler sea air is sucked. Some moist air from the Indian Ocean streams towards the northeast (Indian summer monsoon) and some air from the North Atlantic blows to the south-east. This air moves across the country, gaining height and cooling down, shedding its moisture as rain. Such a European monsoon condition usually lasts until late summer (15th to 20th of August). The rain which starts the seven sleepers rule must not be a local shower however, but a part of generally rainy weather conditions during the end of June or the beginning of July.

The weather rules of countrymen are comparatively reliable, especially when they are short-term, local forecasts. Such rules are usually based on the life-long experience of farmers, hunters and shepherds, who are in constant contact with the weather of their region and know it as intimately as their own fields and forests. One must realise, however, that many of these rules only apply to a strictly limited region and are useless for other areas to which many of them have been carried by word of mouth.

If we look at the weather rules as a whole, we realise that they express the desire of men to understand processes which are outside their comprehension. Even the greatest expert, who knows how to use modern scientific equipment as well as country lore, must admit that we still know too little about the weather to be able to predict it accurately in every case.

There are two reasons for this inability. One is the immeasurability of the atmosphere. It is so large that if every human being had to observe an equal portion of it, each one would have to watch two million tons of air. The second is our ignorance, even in this dawning age of space travel, of the atmospheric events in the stratosphere and the limiting layer between it and the troposphere, called the tropopause. Gas-filled balloons are sent up twice daily from four hundred places, and rise to great heights, sending back constant information about temperatures, humidity and air pressure by means of small ultra short-wave transmitters (Radiosondes). These balloons are followed by radar and give information about wind direction and strength. Exploratory rockets with automatic instruments bring us valuable results from the upper air layers, but all these results are only like pin-pricks on an elephant's hide when seen against the size of the stratosphere; they tell us no more about it than we could tell about the seas if we had only a glassful of sea water. We know little more about the part played by the stratosphere than that it can influence events in the weather zone.

The weather is probably also influenced by events in outer space which have scarcely been investigated. Observations by Australian meteorologists seem to confirm this. The statistics of Dr. E. G. Bowen of Sydney show that at seven control points in different countries persistent rain occurs after the earth has passed through meteor swarms (Geminids, 13th–14 December; Ursids, 22nd December; Quadrantids, 3rd January). Since rain can only fall when a sufficiently humid atmosphere contains microscopic solid particles which enable drops to form, it is possible that the meteoric dust takes on the role of these so-called "condensation nuclei." Bowen's theory is supported by the fact that rain always falls at the control points on the 12th, 22nd and 30th of January, that is 27–30 days after the earth has met the meteor swarms in space. This four-week period corresponds exactly to the time it would take fine dust particles to sink to the weather zone.

How well the meteorologists can foretell the weather, despite all these difficulties, is demonstrated by the fact that eighty-six per cent of their short-term forecasts are said to be correct. This achievement deserves the greatest credit, for only a hundred years ago men felt themselves in servitude

to the weather as if to a dark, demoniacal power, the moods
of which they could neither predict nor control.

The regular weather service which we know to-day owes
its formation to a curious and disastrous accident in the
Black Sea in the nineteenth century. On the 14th of November, 1854, the French and British fleets were blockading the
Russian harbour of Sebastopol. Their plan to occupy the
town after a crushing bombardment was upset by a mighty
windstorm which blew across the sea from the south-west.
The French ship of Line *Henri IV* foundered and the other
vessels were so severely damaged that the attack had to be
called off. The French Minister of War was so dismayed when
the news reached him that he decided to declare war on the
new and unpredictable enemy, and consulted the French
astronomer Leverrier. At first Leverrier merely shrugged his
shoulders, but he promised to think it over. He found out that
the storm had not developed in the Black Sea but had already
traversed a portion of Europe. Since telegraphy already connected most countries of Europe, a telegraphic weather warning could have saved the fleet. Sebastopol fell to the Allies a
year after the catastrophe, but the successful endeavours of
the French astronomer were of much greater value to mankind than the victory, since they called into being (starting in
France) the telegraphic weather service.

Leverrier was the first person to hold that atmospheric
conditions were not merely due to coincidence but had to
follow physical laws. He relied on those laws. In his opinion,
each aspect of weather was the sum of mutually interacting
forces in the air, the theory of which could be understood
if there was a sufficiently close network of observers.

Leverrier's ideas are still valid. Even to-day the greatest
possible number of observation reports about conditions in
the atmosphere are the most important basis for the work of
the weather expert. The more details he has at a given time,
the more accurately he can predict the future development
of the weather. He is helped by about ten thousand meteorological stations, on land and sea, spread over the whole
world. They all co-operate by regularly sending their observations every three hours by a complicated system of
telegraphy, teleprinting and television. Automatic stations,
protected against wind and weather, are placed in inacces-
sible and inhospitable regions, and these transmit their measurements and observations by radio, just as reliably as if
men were working them. The United States Weather
Bureau has unmanned weather stations safely anchored at
many places in the sea. Robust steel robots, as tall as a man,
have been dropped by parachute over the polar regions.

Here they automatically right themselves, become anchored to the ice and regularly transmit the results of observations for several months. Russian technologists have built stations on drifting ice-floes in the Arctic which automatically record the course on which they are drifting. Artificial satellites are specially intended to make observations at a greater height. All these machines replace men where it is impossible to maintain a human crew. They help to make the net of weather stations as closely knit as possible and to give weather forecasts of the greatest possible accuracy.

The information from the individual weather stations is sent to a central office in the form of coded numbers. These are then collected, evaluated and turned into weather-maps and forecasts. All the civilised countries of the world have organised their weather service in this manner. In West Germany, for instance, there are stations in Hamburg, Schleswig, Bremen, Essen-Mühlheim, Frankfurt, Neustadt, Nürnberg, Stuttgart and Munich, with a central office in Offenbach.

Next to the Central Institute for Weather Forecasts in Moscow, the best and most modern central weather office is probably the American National Meteorological Center in Suitland (Maryland), which is under the direction of the United States Weather Bureau in Washington. The place is as busy as a huge beehive. Weather specialists work in shifts around the clock on the many duties of the weather service. It is due to the work at Suitland that the American citizen knows when to take an umbrella to the office; the farmer is told the best times to reap and sow; the sportsman finds the best day for an attempt on a record, and the hostess knows when to plan her garden party without fear of rain. Suitland gives the most up-to-date weather reports to aerodromes, newspapers and radio and television stations, as well as exchanging information with the central weather offices of other nations. This mammoth concern employs more than twenty specialists on the preparation of about sixty daily weather-maps of the American continent alone. These include "high-weather charts" which tell about conditions in the upper layers of the air. A whole section deals with the clicks and Morse signals from the small transmitters carried by stratospheric balloons, which automatically send messages back to earth. Another group of experts deals with the radar apparatus which has become an important tool of modern meteorology.

What is radar, and what has it got to do with the weather? The word is an abbreviation for "Radio-Detecting-and-Ranging," which was developed in the last world war to detect German aircraft. At that time nobody knew that it would become an important part of the weather service. The engineer Bent from the Institute for Ray Research in Massachusetts soon found that radar could locate hail and rainclouds, tornadoes and hurricanes just as accurately as it could aircraft. Bent's experiments demonstrated that the ultra short-waves of radar were reflected, not only by solid bodies but by raindrops. The radar screen shows them as whitish areas, just as it shows a projecting rock in the sea as a bright spot, but the apparatus must work at a certain wave-length to produce useful results. Rays of a wavelength between one and two centimetres (2/5th to 4/5th inches) show the finest water droplets, but their energy is quickly weakened by the humidity of the air and the screen only gives a vague picture. Rays of too great a wavelength, on the other hand, are not reflected sufficiently. The most practical apparatus is one with a wavelength of three to six centimetres (about 1.1/5th to 2.2/5th inches), which will show the spirally shaped rainclouds in the center of a hurricane, for instance, at a distance of about 240 to 300 miles. The dimension, speed and direction of a hurricane can be discovered, and this enables one to warn the islands and coastland areas in its path. Thanks to radar some tornadoes can also be discovered in time and the protective measures, which are started at once, have prevented much damage and loss of life.

Meteorologists have used every possible means that could help them, and their efforts have not been in vain. It has been estimated that more than DM 1000 Million (ca. £80,000,-000) worth of property is saved from destruction every year by the observations of the weather service in West Germany alone. Despite all this, the state of our knowledge is not yet satisfactory, especially with regard to long-term forecasts. The longer a forecast the worse is the result, because small inaccuracies become magnified by the inevitable calculations and thus lead to inaccurate results. The probability of a correct long-term forecast is, therefore, often due not to correct calculations, but to the instinct of an experienced meteorologist and his clever interpretation by comparison with similar conditions that he can recall.

Half a century ago the Norwegian Bjerknes tried to simplify the difficulties of weather forecasting by describing the weather laws in seven mathematical equations. Later these seven grew to ten, but an enormous amount of calculating must be done to solve them. It soon became evident that in practice even a large human staff, or the use of normal calculating machines, could not do the work quickly enough to make it useful. The mathematical evaluation of a single weather condition by the ten equations would have taken several weeks, which rather defeated the object of the forecast.

The calculation of weather, therefore, fell into abeyance until the modern electronic brain was invented. This masterpiece of technology can quickly work out sums the solution of which would take days, or even weeks, when attempted by dozens of mathematicians. The largest electronic brains, which are at the disposal of meteorologists of some countries, are giants built up of steel, wire and electronic tubes. They can carry out 8000–9000 additions, 1200 multiplications or 500 divisions per second, and can even print weather-maps showing future conditions. Magnetic bands, up to 2300 feet long, store the results electrically, each inch of band containing about 200 numbers. These values can be used directly for new calculations or given out as intermediate results. They perform a task the speed and accuracy of which can never be equalled by human brains, even when working as a team.

Even the help of electronic brains does not enable us to predict weather with absolute certainty. The apparently insuperable difficulty is that these machines must be fed by men, fed with their raw material, the open-sesame formula of present weather conditions, the numbers for the ten weather equations. Who can guarantee that these values are correct to the second or third decimal place? These initial values are liable to be slightly inaccurate, which is inevitable with difficult meteorological measurements, and it is these inaccuracies, as I said before, which become magnified during the calculations and invalidate the final result. In addition to this the equations do not contain all of the factors which determine weather, such as radiation, friction, etc., nor can they deal with the fact that a mass of air can change its direction and speed half a dozen times in two hours. The so-called numerical prediction only gives weather charts a few days in advance and from these the meteorologists must tediously work out the coming weather.

This is the Achilles heel of weather forecasting. At this point demands are made on the human brain which cannot always be met, even by experience. Don't curse if the prediction in your daily paper is not always accurate. Don't be annoyed if it rains on a Sunday for which fine weather was forecast. The weather men, as Professor Schmauss has so aptly put it, are like sharp shooters who are daily given a new rifle and expected to score a bull's-eye with the first shot. As you may know from personal experience, that is not easy.

11

ARTIFICIAL WEATHER

WOULDN'T IT BE PLEASANT if one could simply press a button to make it rain or snow, or produce thunderstorms or sunshine? What hasn't man done to make this dream come true? All through the ages he has tried to "make his own weather," or at least to influence it according to his wishes. Since the dawn of history he has tried to placate the weather gods when they seemed angry. The brain of primitive man, unburdened by chemistry and physics, interpreted sunshine, rain, thunder, wind and snow as moods of a supernatural being whose presence eluded him. Since he believed the gods to have feelings similar to his own, he tried to appease their fury with presents, and thus exchange good weather for bad.

Although many atmospheric processes are still hardly clearer than in the age of votive offerings, modern meteorologists nevertheless know enough to use the weather for their own purposes on certain occasions. When conditions are right, for instance, they can literally make rain. The prerequisite is sufficient humidity, for without enough moisture nothing can be done. The cleverest "weather maker" cannot milk the moisture from the air when the humidity is too low. In other words the air must either already contain water vapour or else it must be filled by artificial evaporation; but to produce even a small rain cloud in a dry atmosphere requires an enormous amount of effort. Expressed in numbers this means that to produce a rain cloud with a volume of one cubic mile in dry air, more than four thousand tons of water must be evaporated. This is equivalent to a mighty basin full of water 30 feet wide, 20 feet deep and at least 200 feet long. Who would go to so much trouble?

This method of producing appreciable amounts of rain is, therefore, pointless. There is another way, however; to derive it from existing clouds, which for one reason or another are not prepared to shed the water they contain.

To follow this method we have to understand what happens to the moisture in the air. If you place a bowl of water in a room, you will notice that after a few days the water has grown less. We say it has evaporated. Physicists know that evaporation means the escape of water molecules into the air, where they continue their existence as a gas. In this manner, water is converted into colourless and invisible water vapour or steam (the white clouds from a boiling kettle are steam which has already condensed into droplets of water).

The air cannot take up unlimited amounts of water vapour, but only a certain quantity, which is determined by the volume and temperature of the air. Two hundred cubic feet of air, for instance, can take up about an ounce of water vapour at freezing point, but approximately three and a half times that amount at 20° C. When these values are reached the air has become saturated. Further additions of water vapour or cooling of the air usually turns the gas back into liquid form, as droplets on the wall, dew on the ground or as fog.

The clouds give a splendid example, by their constant appearance and disappearance in the sky above us, of the changeability of water vapour. The volatile gas does not always and automatically change into droplets, however, even when it should do so according to the above explanation. Before it can condense, the air must contain minute dust or salt particles on which the gaseous water can form a sort of skin; only then will droplets be formed.

The air usually contains enough of these impurities, or condensation nuclei, to enable the water vapour to change into droplets. Above large industrial towns each cubic inch of air contains about two and a half million of them, excluding the larger dust particles. Despite this there are cases when the super-saturated air cannot form clouds. Sometimes the exhaust gases from aeroplanes play the part of the condensation nuclei and cause the comet-like white tails which we call "condensation trails." Taken as a whole clouds and fog are nothing but a collection of tiny water droplets in the air, and if you want further details, the size of the cloud-forming droplets varies between 0.1 and 0.001 millimetre (about 1/25th to 1/2500th inches). They are created from water vapour by the cooling or supersaturation of air in the presence of condensation nuclei.

Although clouds consist of droplets, we know that not all of them bring rain. Some droplets are too small and light to fall down and, apart from this, upward currents of air help to keep them suspended, causing the droplets at the edge of a cloud to evaporate and re-form continuously. It may also happen that several of them combine and become heavy enough to fall from the cloud, reaching the earth as fine Scotch mist.

Proper rain, consisting of large drops, has little in common with this fine misty rain; it comes from high clouds in which the temperature can fall well below freezing point. In such clouds the drops of water usually change to ice crystals or snowflakes (even in summer). When they have reached a certain weight they fall, melt in the warmer air below the cloud and reach the earth as rain. If the air between the cloud and the earth is too cold to melt them, they fall as hail or snow.

It is the large raindrops that farmers value most, for rain of this type brings the essential water in its most effective form. Town-dwellers may dislike it, but farmers and foresters complain if it stays away too long. Sometimes rain-heavy clouds drift, almost mockingly, over the parched earth without shedding their precious load. How can this happen? Either because the ice crystals or snow flakes are not heavy enough to fall against the up-currents, or because snow and ice crystals have not yet formed. This brings us to a curious fact. Water inside a cloud may not solidify although the temperature is well below freezing point. You can repeat this trick of nature on a small scale if you wish to. If you carefully cool some pure (distilled) water in a bowl, it will remain fluid even below 0° C. By placing small pieces of a solid into the supercooled water you can cause the whole bowl to turn to ice immediately, while the temperature will rise to freezing point. The truth of the matter is, that the water in the bowl, just like the droplets in the cloud, needs small impurities, or seeds, before turning to ice at temperatures below freezing point.

By taking this into consideration, the modern rain-maker can easily trick rainbearing clouds into shedding their water. He needs only to introduce a large number of seeds into them. If he succeeds many droplets will turn to ice and snow, gain weight, fall down and melt into rain on their passage through the warmer air.

The first thing to do is to find clouds which are suitable for such treatment, supercooled cumulus clouds. Nowadays one does this by exploring their interiors with radar in order to find their suitability and the most favourable time for action. When this has been determined, an aeroplane or rocket is sent up to inoculate the cloud by sprinkling it with "dry ice" (solid carbon dioxide, temperature −75° C.) or better still, with silver iodide. Both these substances act as seeds and cause clouds to shed their rain, when they had no intention of doing so without help.

Many successes have been achieved in this manner according to American reports. In one instance the city fathers of New York called on the rain expert Dr. Howell in the summer of 1949, when the town was suffering from drought and water rationing was imminent. Howell's experiments were followed by several sustained rainfalls which ended the water scarcity. In another case American rain-makers are said to have earned six thousand dollars by quenching a forest fire in the Tillamook region (Oregon) with artificial rain. The fire would have cost many millions of dollars if it had spread any farther.

Places that are threatened with cloud bursts or hailstorms can also be protected from damage by artificial rain. Such damaging weather occurs when thunder or hail clouds develop undisturbed until they reach dangerous proportions. The upward winds in the clouds' centre then play with the ice granules (like ping-pong balls on jets of water at a shooting gallery), until they have reached considerable size by adding one layer of ice after another on to themselves (in 1929 hailstones larger than tennis balls fell in Durban, South Africa). If the upward currents cease suddenly, the cloud empties itself instantaneously, like a split sack of corn, shedding a rattling, damaging mass of hailstones. If the air below the cloud is warm enough the hailstones melt and hit the ground as a cloud burst.

Such discharges can be prevented if the cloud is inoculated in time (with silver iodide for instance), but this depends on the exact moment, which must be before ice granules have formed; in other words action can only be successful when the cloud consists solely of supercooled water droplets. In that case the silver iodide leads to ice formation at a moment when the upwinds are not strong enough to blow the granules continuously upwards, thus making them grow to a dangerous size. Instead the ice granules fall quickly, melt below the cloud and reach the earth as harmless rain.

Marvellous, we exclaim when we see a cloud suddenly deposit its wet freight after being inoculated. It is admittedly a small marvel, for we have the means to milk a cloud, but have we really fulfilled the age-old dream of mankind? Let us not delude ourselves; by outwitting a cloud we have only subjugated nature at one tiny point. We have not made "weather" in the larger sense of the word. Our present-day methods are quite inadequate to influence weather as a whole, such as turning a rainy summer into a sunny one. This will probably remain the case, for the forces required are enormously large. Calculations have shown that even the power of an H-bomb would not be nearly enough to produce one of the typical low pressure areas often met in Western Europe. Apart from creating radiation and radio-active dust (see page 171) an atom bomb, considered as a source of energy, can have only a limited local weather effect, and not the far-reaching one it is often believed to possess.

12

THE CAVE OF ÆOLUS

IN THE FAIRY STORIES, SAGAS AND FOLK-TALES OF ALL NATIONS
the wind plays the part of a supernatural power. It has as
many names as it has voices, and any attempt to describe
them all would be idle, but some special winds and storms
have always influenced the fate of man. They have cooled
sun-baked towns, brought rainclouds to the parched earth or
caused death and destruction. These are the winds I shall
talk about.

If you have spent a summer holiday by the seaside and
kept your weather eye on the wind you may have noticed a
curious thing. In the early morning there is calm; the sea
lies quiet and only tiny waves lap the shore. As the sun rises
higher and higher the wind also rises, hardly noticeably at
first but constantly growing stronger. A breeze blows in from
the sea and causes the waves to grow larger. It reaches its
height in the afternoon and dies away in the evening. During the night the wind turns right round and blows from the
land out to sea.

You do not need to be very clever to find the explanation
of this mysterious air movement. When the sun rises in the
morning its rays warm the land more quickly than the water.
Since warm air weighs less than cold air it rises and causes
an area of low pressure, or Low, over the land, which acts
like a vacuum cleaner and sucks air inland from the sea,
giving rise to the sea breeze. The opposite happens at night.
Since land warms more quickly it also cools faster than the
sea, and the air above the sea is soon warmer than that over
the land. A Low now develops over the sea and sucks in air
from the land. This night-wind blows until morning when
the temperature of land and sea are the same and the air
comes to rest, only to begin the same cycle all over again a
few hours later.

This is an example in miniature of the famous monsoons
which play an important part, sometimes beneficial and sometimes dangerous, in many regions of the earth.

The word monsoon is derived from the Arabic *mausim*,
meaning season, and refers to those mighty winds, blowing
across the great land and sea masses, which change summer
and winter. If the daily path of the sun causes the small

land and sea breezes, the seasonal difference in warmth between the land and sea masses causes the great monsoons. It is probable that other circumstances also play a part, according to some scientists even a decisive one, in their creation. Among these influences is the poleward shift of the equatorial low pressure belt in the respective hemisphere, and the seasonal shift of the planetary winds as a whole. The detailed effects of these influences are not yet known.

The most important and most thoroughly investigated seasonal wind is the Indian summer monsoon. It owes its being, at least in part, to the huge Low which exists over Central Asia during the hot season. This Low sucks in air from the cooler seas, including the Indian Ocean. On its passage across the sea, where the captains of sailing ships have used it for two millenia, it is deflected to the east by the earth's rotation and arrives at the mainland as a south-west wind. That is why it is also called the south-west monsoon, or simply Sou'-wester.

As India forms the border region between the Asiatic land mass and the Indian Ocean, its fate is bound up with the summer monsoon (East Asia is in a similar position). It is the monsoon, eagerly awaited, which brings rain to the peasants after a period of devastating drought. During its passage across the ocean it has absorbed enormous amounts of moisture which it sheds over the land. Monsoon is a magic word to the inhabitants and means much more to them than spring to us. If the monsoon arrives too late, too weakly or too suddenly it can cause harvest failures and famines, which may result in the deaths of many thousands.

The first barrier which the advancing monsoon clouds meet is the Western Ghats, a mountain chain on the south-west coast of India. Here, on the mountain sides facing the sea, is staged the first act of the great annual drama. The clouds are piled up by the mountains and forced to gain height. This cools them down, and they shed part of their moisture as torrential rain. During the monsoon months the Ghats have a monsoon rainfall of between 120 and 280 inches, an amount sufficient to support a jungle, despite the long dry winter period from December to May.

Crossing the Ghats, the monsoon clouds continue their journey over the plateau of the Dekkan in Central India. They shed more of their rain and moisten the parched soil.

But the most dramatic act is still to come. It takes place in the north-east corner of the country where the clouds enter a sort of blind alley in the valley of the Brahmaputra. Here, wedged in between the walls of the Himalayas in the north and the Patkoi mountains in the east, lies the province

A section from the earth's crust, approximately 200,000 square miles in size, photographed from a rocket 100 miles up; the large dark area on the upper left is the Gulf of California.

These strange cloud formations, which occur frequently along the forefront of a thunderstorm, are called squall lines. There are strong vertical movements of air inside. Gusts occur frequently where such clouds appear. *Below:* Three beautiful thunderstorm clouds (cumulo-nimbus) over the sea. They originated from rising warm air. The anvil-shaped flattening is caused by a temperature inversion layer in the air which prevents the clouds from rising further.

Northern lights can assume all sorts of shapes. The pictures on this page show some examples. *Left:* A sheet-like aurora, changing its shape continuously; it appeared like a curtain hanging in the sky and moving slowly in the wind. *Below left:* A flickering pale green northern light resembling an undulating gown.

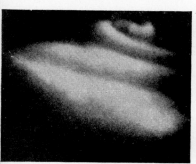

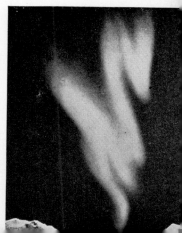

Above right: A northern, or polar, light (aurora borealis), which has a bluish fluorescence. All the rays seem to converge at a central point. *Right:* Another common shape, where the rays seem to form rotating sheets.

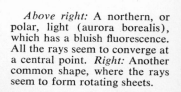

Above: Lenticular clouds (lenticularis) formed under föhn conditions which descend slowly. This movement is faster at the periphery of the clouds, causing the rims to evaporate more rapidly than the centre.

A stratus layer seen from above; in the foreground, a pontoon of a reconnaissance seaplane.

Festoon-like clouds (mammato-cumuli), formed by a cold downdraft near the edge of a thunderstorm.

Cirrus clouds above Lake Zeller, Austria; small cumulus clouds above the mountains.

A föhn cloud over a mountain range in New Zealand.

A mock sun on the right; the true sun on the left is a milky spot.

Warbler in flight with an insect in its mouth.

Seed dispersal of dandelions.

The same region of cloud before and, twenty minutes later, after a seeding operation.

Above: An impressive view of a tornado near Jasper, Minnesota. Like a giant elephant's trunk, gyrating with incredible speed, the storm moves slowly across the earth. Alternately expanding and contracting, it produces a grinding, thundering noise and leaves a 150-foot swath of destruction behind. *Right:* When tornadoes are formed over the sea the whirling air masses suck water to a height of a thousand feet or more. This picture shows such a tornado, known as a waterspout, over the Gulf of Mexico.

A thunderstorm in full fury. This picture was exposed for several minutes and shows numerous bolts of lightning at a glance. Some lightning, flashing inside the clouds, illuminates them from within. To the rear at the left are the strange mammato-cumuli.

Above: A weather-plane on its flight into the centre of a hurricane. The inset shows a hurricane on the radarscope. The rain clouds spiralling around the "eye" of the storm are clearly discernible. *Below:* New York in the fog. If the air cannot move vertically, fog combines with the exhaust gases from the city, forming "smog."

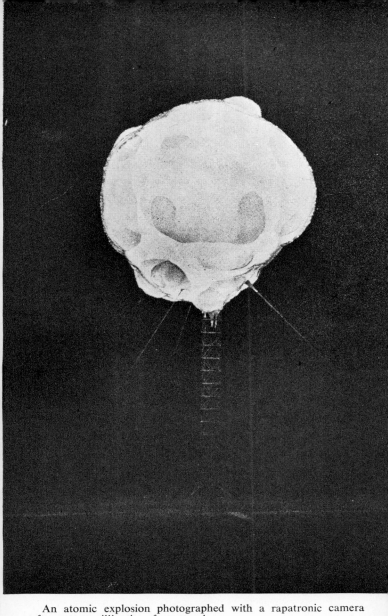

An atomic explosion photographed with a rapatronic camera after seven millionths of a second.

Two stages in the growth of the cloud from the first atomic
bomb detonated under water.

Opposite: Atomic mushroom cloud.

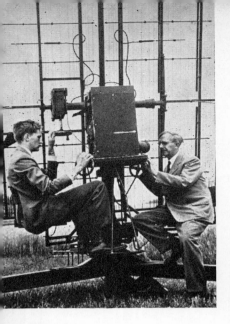

Below: A radio probe, a meteorological measuring device, has risen on a balloon and automatically recorded barometric pressure, temperature, and humidity. A built-in transmitter has relayed the information back to the ground. In this picture the probe is parachuting back to earth. Note the antenna below the probe. The white reflector allows the ground station (*above*) to pinpoint the radio probe by means of radar. It is possible to follow the weather balloon by radar and get information on the air currents at various altitudes.

of Assam. It is a country which can only be described as a cleverly constructed death-trap for monsoon clouds. Here they are encircled and cannot escape, except over the sky-towering peaks. The water-heavy clouds are herded and pushed, like angry animals, into a cage that is too small for them, while a steady stream of newcomers intrudes from the south-west. Finally, because there is no alternative, they try to escape. They scramble up the mountainsides, jettisoning their water in torrents as if it were trying to hinder their flight. A seemingly endless deluge descends, accompanied by thunder and lightning. There is no comparison anywhere on earth with this annual drama. The small town of Cherrapunji, for instance, in the Khasi Hills, has an average annual rainfall of about 460 inches, thirteen times more than Munich, and must be one of the wettest places in the world.

During the monsoon rains the traffic in many parts of India stops completely. Many harbours on the coast of Malabar close for the season. Sometimes masses of water pour from the sky almost unceasingly for forty or fifty days, until the streets are flooded to knee-height and everything becomes waterlogged. The thatched roofs of the houses rot away, wood swells, clothes and foodstuffs moulder, epidemics of plague break out. Beythan, who knows India well, reports that even amphibious creatures such as frogs, try to escape the moisture-laden air and find a dry spot in the houses.

But all this is nothing compared to the blessing which the monsoon brings to the arid land. This is the hour of the rice farmer. Now that the soil is thoroughly soaked, it can be ploughed and the rice seedlings planted. During the planting the women paddle ankle-deep in the mud and pray to heaven that the rain may continue, for up to the time of ripening the rice must stand in eight to twelve inches of water if the harvest is to be a good one.

The Indian monsoon rains last, in varying strength, up to the beginning of September; then they die away. The monsoon "retreats," as the experts say. By this they mean that it turns around and blows in winter from the high pressure area in north-east Asia towards the south-west. This north-east monsoon is much weaker than its summer brother, for the Himalayas in the north and the mountains of Burma in the east break its force. It varies in strength all over India and except for south-east India does not bring rain, for it comes from the dry areas of Asia and only passes over the sea for a short time in the Bay of Bengal. It announces the dry season.

Monsoon-like winds also develop in North America, parts of Africa, Australia and the Caspian Sea. Under certain circumstances we even speak of a monsoon condition in Europe, when rainy weather spoils our summer. Wherever these streams of air occur, wherever they relieve the monotony of the climate, they act as a revivifying gift of nature.

If the monsoon is longed and prayed for, there are other winds which are less welcome, even if not actually destructive. Amongst these is the hot, dusty Sirocco (also known in North Africa as the Ghibli) which occurs on the frontal end, or both ends, of a wandering Low. It usually comes from the south or the south-east and has a different name in different countries. The Egyptians call it Samum, the Spaniards Leveche, and the Arabs Chamsin, which means fifty, for it usually appears fifty days after the spring and autumn equinox.

The inhabitants of the Mediterranean countries fear the Sirocco because of its enervating effects and the masses of sand and dust which it brings from the dry regions of Africa. It can become a full-grown sandstorm. No hole or crack is too fine for the sand to penetrate, it enters everywhere, filling ears and nostrils, irritating the eyes, damaging car engines and stopping aeroplane flights. In Sicily the Sirocco is filled with a sticky, salty moisture which it has gathered during its passage across the Mediterranean, and which seems to make breathing difficult.

The Mediterranean harbours many winds which are caused or influenced in strength and direction by peculiarities of the landscape. Among these winds is the Föhn, a warm, dry, descending mountain wind, usually blowing strongly and gustily, accompanied by a cloud cover (Föhn-wall) above the mountains.

The Föhn has been most thoroughly investigated in the Alps. People north of the mountains call it the South Föhn and those to the south the North Föhn.

Let us examine the South Föhn in the northern Alps, the "snow devourer," whose hot, dry breath can affect our moods and well-being so unfavourably. It begins as rising, humid air south of the Alps, losing ½° C. for every three hundred feet of height gained, forming clouds, crossing the mountains and losing moisture as it descends into the valleys, and gaining 1° C. for every three hundred feet of height lost.

The unexpected arrival of a Föhn can lead to surprising natural events. Let us imagine a winter day. The night before the temperature was well below freezing point. All the alpine foothills are coated in crisp, crackling white. Suddenly the power of the frost is broken. High in the mountains a roaring noise begins which approaches on the wind. At the same time the peaks seem to come closer, their violet-black outline clearly showing against the deep blue sky as the Föhn sucks up the last remnants of cloud and converts them into vapour.

This wind has an insatiable appetite for moisture. After it has devoured the clouds in the sky, it starts on the snow of the forests and fields. The thaw begins. A task which would take the sun several days is done, almost playfully, by the Föhn in a few hours. Beneath its hot, dry breath the winter's snow melts so rapidly that torrents roar into the villages and avalanches thunder from the mountains. Down in the valley where the air lies like a peaceful lake, the Föhn advances in turbulent gusts, and relentlessly thrusts it to the north.

The warm wind blowing down the northern slopes of the Alps is as shortlived as it is violent. Only when it comes towards the end of winter does it bring spring and more permanent warmth. Normally its reign is short, for cold air from the west usually breaks the power of the southern invader after a few days. Dark clouds appear in the west, as if warning the intruder, and a wedge of cold air advances inexorably across country, pushing the Föhn back where it came from. Soon after that new snow begins to fall. Winter has returned.

There is sometimes a similar wind on the south side of the Alps called the North Föhn. This falling wind occurs especially in late winter, when cold air from the northern side plunges over the Alps and grows warmer as it descends. The North Föhn does not affect men as unfavourably as its southern brother, but its heat is not sufficient to warm the people in the valleys. Compared to the temperatures which are prevalent in the southern alpine regions the North Föhn is still cool. This is the fault of the Alps themselves, which act as a sort of barrier, preventing the exchange of air in a north-south direction. It frequently happens that you approach the Gotthardt tunnel from the north in cold rainy weather, to emerge twelve minutes later on the south side in brilliant sunshine.

The Bora, a cold wind found on the mountainous coast of the Adriatic, the Ægean and the Black Sea, is related to the North Föhn. As a true falling wind it also warms up as it descends the hillsides, but it comes from such cold regions that the warming up is not enough to give the impression of a hot wind. The Adriatic harbour of Trieste is frequently visited by the Bora which brings cold air, snow and ice in its train. At its worst it can stop all traffic.

Another falling wind is the notorious Mistral of southeastern France. It is stormy, cold and dry, and is created when there is a High over Central France and a Low over the Gulf of Lions. It is the scourge of the Provence, an unpleasant surprise which appears unexpectedly and causes people to shiver and sets their nerves on edge. The town of Avignon in the lower Rhône valley is most frequently troubled by it.

More dangerous are the two Asian snowstorms, the dreaded Purga and Buran, which, like the blizzards of North America, usually come from the north or the north-east. W. Köppen has said that during a Purga the air is "a chaos of moving, hard snow dust which closes the eyes." Only a forest can afford some protection and where there is none, men and animals must trust their luck and lie down, to be covered by snow until the storm is over. It is impossible to orientate one's self during these storms and it has happened that people have been frozen to death, very close to their homes, because they could not find their way back.

With the exception of the saturated ones, all winds have the property of increasing the evaporation of water. When a wind blows across the land it sucks up the moisture of the soil and becomes an enemy of the many plants whose leaves are not protected against evaporation. Examples of this are the winds of the deserts and steppes, which often leave parched areas behind them when they exceed their usual limits and reach those regions where plants have not become adapted to arid conditions over millions of years. The Norther of South Australia and the Suchowéj of the Southern Russian steppes are notorious for such action.

Evenly blowing winds are the strongest motivating force of the ocean currents. They pile up the water into waves big enough to contain whole department stores. The longer the distance over which the wind drives a wave, the longer the "fetch" and the larger the mass of water. The largest wave of which there is trustworthy record reached a height of 111½ feet. It was seen during a Pacific gale in 1933 by the ship's officer R. Carson of the U.S.S. *Ramapo* who measured it against a mark on the mast.

Steady winds of a certain force cause sandstorms. They also work on the seashores, laying out patterns or ripples. In this they compete with the rollers from the sea which fold the ocean bed as if with curling irons.

It is the winds which carry the enormous swarms of locusts over long distances and thus bring harvest failures and famine. The largest swarm of locusts to reach Great Britain in recent years was still over the Canary Islands on 15th October, 1954. Nobody was expecting any trouble, when suddenly they arrived over the Scilly Islands two days later. The

Wind Force according to Beaufort	Name	Signs	Average velocity in miles per hour
0	Calm	Smoke rises vertically	0
1	Light air	Direction shown by smoke but not by vanes	1–3
2	Slight breeze	Leaves rustle, vanes move	4–7
3	Gentle breeze	Leaves and twigs moved	8–12
4	Moderate breeze	Raises dust and moves small branches	13–18
5	Fresh breeze	Small trees begin to sway	19–24
6	Strong breeze	Large branches moved, telephone wires whistle	25–31
7	High wind	Whole trees in motion	32–38
8	Fresh gale	Twigs broken off. Walking difficult.	39–46
9	Strong gale	Slight structural damage. Chimney-pots removed.	47–54
10	Whole gale	Trees uprooted. Great structural damage	55–63
11	Storm	Wide spread damage	64–75
12	Hurricane	Countryside devastated. Winds in this class only in tropical storms in West Indies, U.S.A., Far Eastern waters and Antarctic blizzards	Over 75

insects could not have made the journey under their own power; the wind's direction and velocity indicated quite clearly that it had been responsible for bringing them.

The winds, being invisible and formless, would utterly elude our comprehension were it not for the two properties which enable us to measure and apply controls to them, their direction and strength. The direction of the wind is always taken as that from which it comes and not that to which it is going. The ancient Greeks gave special names to the various directions, and only in the reign of Charlemagne were the winds classified according to the four main points of the compass. Nowadays the intermediate values are also used, such as northeast, east-south-east, west-south-west, etc., so that winds are named according to thirty-two compass points.

The strength of the wind is measured with an anemometer, of which one type consists of two crossed sticks, to the ends of which four hemispherical cups have been attached. This cross revolves horizontally on a vertical axis, and turns at a speed which increases with the force of the wind. It is connected to an apparatus which records the wind velocity. This makes it possible to classify winds according to their strength into the twelve categories of the "Beaufort" scale. (See page 101.)

The effects of certain winds have not been included in the scale, for they are so cataclysmic that they cannot be classified. They seem to be the work of the devil, mysterious in their origin and treacherous in their behaviour. They are dealt with in the next few chapters.

13

TORNADO

MAN HAS TRIED AGAIN AND AGAIN to harness the wind for his own pleasure and profit. He has built windmills which drive millstones or complicated electric generators, and he has constructed ships and aeroplanes to make the best use of the air streams. The winds help him in matters great and small, but he does not have them completely under control. Some of them leave him helpless and make a mock of his ingenuity, wisdom and technical knowledge. Some atmospheric conditions can create air movements of almost unbelievable force and when faced by these, man is merely a helpless dwarf who can only pray for deliverance.

One of these frightful winds is the tornado. Originally the name only referred to the stormy squalls on the edge of rotating storms on the African Gold Coast. Nowadays we call all the extraordinary violent whirlwinds of small diameter "tornado." They occur most frequently in Australia and the United States, but are also known in Europe. They are accompanied by characteristic, funnel shaped "tornado-clouds."

To this day we do not know exactly how a tornado originates. The American weather expert W. J. Humphreys believes that at least twenty-six different conditions have to be fulfilled before a tornado can develop. It is certain that extremely hot air must meet cold air before a tornado can be produced, and it is probable that the so-called jet-streams (see Chapter 15) also play an important part in their creation.

Some areas seem to be particularly favourably constructed for the development of tornadoes, and one of these is the Mississippi basin (see diagram). In this area the very warm, humid air from the Gulf of Mexico streams northward without hindrance and meets Pacific air which has been cooled by its high passage over the mountains, thus giving rise to atmospheric conditions not met anywhere else on earth.

The Mississippi region suffered one of its most catastrophic tornadoes on the 23rd of March, 1952. Exceptionally hot, moist air collided with a stream of cold air coming from the North over the State of Arkansas. The two air masses met like two men hurrying in different directions. They became locked together and tried to pass each other. Witnesses on the ground saw ghostly white clouds and oily-black vapour formations all jumbled together in the sky. Soon the air began to whirl upwards, slowly at first but gathering speed. It behaved like liquid water stirred in a pot, rising higher up the sides the faster it is stirred. The whirling motion pressed the air outwards leaving a centre of increasingly rarefied and cold air (air becomes colder as it grows rarefied). As a result of the cooling, the water vapour condensed and formed clouds which were thrown outwards from the centre until they combined into a rotating ring which soon took on the shape of a tube.

Not long after that the tubular cloud turned into a funnel, resembling the dirty grey trunk of an enormous elephant which was fumbling its way towards the ground. At the same time, the air immediately above the ground began to move. Dried leaves whirled upwards. A similar but transparent structure of warm air was feeling its way upward towards

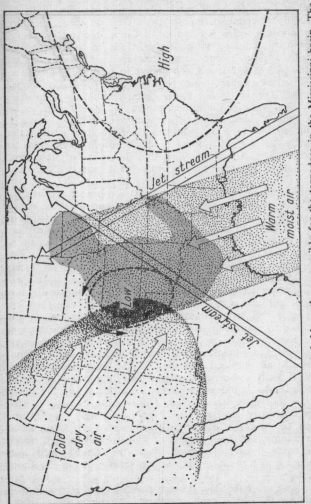

Nowadays high jet-streams are held partly responsible for the tornadoes in the Mississippi basin. The shaded zone shows the area worst hit in 1957.

the funnel. The parts combined, and the transparent lower portion turned into a tube of thick cloud. When fully formed the tornado hung bent in the sky like a supernatural bow. The next thing that happened was that five more tornado tubes grew downward from the clouds, producing on an eyewitness the effect of "rolling along like six reeling drunkards. They made a thunderous noise like the rattle of a thousand freight trains."

The first victim was a policeman who was trying to give a last minute warning to the town of Dyersburg (Tennessee). As he was driving along one of the tornadoes picked up his car and flung it two hundred yards with the wheels upwards. The policeman was killed instantly. Immediately afterwards the tornado tore through the little town with a grinding roar. Men, animals and roof tiles were tossed together. Telephone poles snapped, the wool was torn from grazing sheep, houses caved in and mile-wide areas were shaved bare in fields and forest. Another whirling wind sucked a man through an open window and hung him by his heels in a forked branch. A mass of dust, twigs, fence poles, and bits of metal whipped through the streets, killing everything in its path. With apocalyptic fury the tornadoes raged through the States of Arkansas, Tennessee, Alabama, Kentucky, Mississippi and Missouri. Two hundred and fifty people lost their lives, more than two thousand were injured and several thousand left homeless. The material damage amounted to several million dollars.

Nine hundred and sixty-one tornadoes hit the United States alone during the "record" year of 1957. In 1953 also there were several bad ones, notably that which struck Waco (Texas) on the 11th of May. During the afternoon floods of rain masked the noise of the approaching storm. Nobody was prepared when suddenly the first houses collapsed. Several seconds later 113 people were dead and many hundreds injured. Not a house was left standing on a nine hundred foot wide track straight across the town.

A tornado often only measures thirty to one hundred and fifty feet across and has a maximum width of 1300 feet. It moves across the country at between six and thirty-six miles an hour, can last from five seconds to three hours and cover distances of up to three hundred miles. Its track is often only as wide as a street, but the damage is then all the more severe. North America suffered no less than 5034 tornadoes in the years of 1916 to 1949, which caused 7892 deaths. The average annual death-rate in the U.S.A. due to these "raging elephant trunks" is, therefore, 232. Luckily this number is lower to-day, since excellent storm warnings are in operation and there are many safety cellars in the danger areas.

The destructive force of a tornado consists mainly of two factors: pressure at the edge and suction in the centre. Physicists have calculated that wind pressure increases in proportion to the square of the wind velocity. This means that a storm with 60 mile per hour winds (force 11) presses four times as hard against the wall of a house as a storm with 30-mile per hour winds (force 7).

Our present knowledge about the forces inside a tornado consists only of estimates, since no measuring instrument could withstand its full force. Let us call the wind scale to our aid. A storm of force ten blows at about fifty miles per hour and can uproot trees. Judging by the damage it causes, the vortex of a tornado can attain a speed ten to twelve times greater. This means that it exerts a pressure roughly one hundred times greater than a storm of wind force 10. Under such circumstances small objects can become dangerous missiles. During the American catastrophe of 1952 a tornado picked up ears of wheat and drove them like nails into tree trunks. Sand and grit, whirled up by the air, can penetrate men and animals like buckshot. Tin-plates which are picked up by the raging element are turned into razor-blades and mow down everything in their path. In one case a tornado picked up a refrigerator weighing seven hundredweight and carried it through the air nearly three miles before dropping it back on the ground. In his book *The Elements Rage*, Frank W. Lane cites a case which demonstrates the astonishing power of a tornado. In 1937 a man went to the United States Weather Bureau and asked Dr. Humphreys, the director, "Can what I saw really have happened . . . a tornado lifting a heavy railway engine from one set of rails and depositing it on another?" Humphreys had to confirm that according to his experiences this all but incredible occurrence was actually possible.

The suction in the centre of a tornado is even more uncanny, because harder to understand, than the wind pressure. The centrifugal force constantly pulls the air outwards and creates a strong low pressure area, or partial vacuum, in the centre of the vortex. People inside this area could literally burst, because the human body is adapted to the air pressure which normally exists on the surface of the earth and if this pressure is suddenly removed all the hollow spaces in the body expand uncontrollably. A man in this situation undergoes the same fate as a deep-sea fish that has been brought too swiftly to the surface. The fish is affected because the external pressure of the water has been suddenly removed and, because it cannot adapt itself quickly enough, it swells. It will suffer from "tympanitis," the symptoms of which are a distended body, damaged tissues and a burst swim-bladder. Wherever the suction of a tornado meets air-filled hollow spaces they will explode for the same reason. Houses collapse outwards, gasometers spring leaks, trunks, cupboards and car tyres burst with a loud bang.

One curious event occurred on the 22nd of June, 1928, when Will Keller, a farmer from Greensburg (Kansas) looked up into the vortex of a tornado without being hurt. Between three and four o'clock in the afternoon Keller saw three tornadoes approaching him. He stopped working and hurried to the safety cellar, but before closing the door he cast a glance backward. He saw that the vortex had left the ground. "A few seconds later," reports Keller, "the shaggy end of the funnel was suspended immediately above me. It gave off a gas-like smell and I could hardly breathe. I looked straight into the middle of the funnel. The centre was almost empty, the walls consisted of madly whirling clouds. Lightning jumped from one side to the other. After the tornado had passed over me it came down again and damaged my neighbour's house and barn. The wreckage whirled through the air."

Another form of tornado, usually less dangerous, is the waterspout at sea. It also is formed when warm and cold air meet each other. An eye-witness reports of two such phenomena in the Gulf of Finland.

"In the north-west I saw a mass of clouds, blue-black in colour, and immediately afterwards two terrifying cones. The cones turned into columns of water and one of these monsters advanced towards us. It was a fearful sight. The drops, of which the cylinder consisted, did not fall vertically but seemed to flow down with a screw-like motion only to wind upwards again. Its base seemed to rest in a hollow bowl at the edge of which the sea boiled furiously. The noise was deafening. However, the monster roared harmlessly above and past us and only splashed us with a few cherry-sized raindrops, leaving behind a smell of sulphur and saltpetre."

The speed of rotation of a waterspout is not nearly as great as that of a tornado and is estimated at a maximum of 60 to 120 miles per hour. Waterspouts sometimes collapse after only ten or twenty seconds. Occasionally they occur in groups. When they hit the coast they frequently turn into tornadoes, and the American Westrom describes one at Norfolk (Virginia) which changed repeatedly from one to the other. It began as a tornado, then it sucked a small river-bed dry while turning into a waterspout, changed back into a

tornado, became a waterspout in the harbour and destroyed
some installations, upset some freight-cars on land as a
tornado, and finally raced off across Chesapeake Bay as a
waterspout.

Witnesses have described the noise of a waterspout as
roaring, hissing, crashing and humming. The height and
diameter vary considerably. At Rabat, on the Moroccan coast,
a waterspout reached a height of nearly a thousand feet.
The English sea captain Raplin reports a waterspout near
the coast of Northern Australia, which became very long,
swayed and coiled like a snake. Another eye-witness observed a waterspout at sea during the night flooded with an
unearthly white glow and gliding across the ocean like a
wandering pillar of light. The explanation is simple. The
ghostly illumination was caused by the billions of tiny, lumi-
nescent animals *(Noctiluca)* which live in warm seas.
These animals, which cause the phosphorescence in those
waters, had been sucked up with the water and caused the
waterspout to glow.

14

HURRICANE

THE AIR CAN GENERATE NO GREATER FORCE in a relatively
small space than that developed by a tornado. The wind
velocities of a hurricane are much smaller, but it causes
even greater devastation because its dimensions are very
much larger. A tornado and a hurricane can be compared to
a pouncing tiger and a steamroller.

Even an atomic explosion is a weakling compared to the
raging furies which nature creates every year on the Pacific
and Atlantic Oceans. The hurricane is the worst of all storms,
and a single one can cause a force of five billion horse-power,
the equivalent to many atom bombs of the Hiroshima type, to
rampage across the earth. During the single hurricane catastrophe at Galveston (Texas) in September 1900 the storm
which hit the American coast had sufficient energy to drive all
the power stations in the world for four years.

A hurricane is as mysterious as it is demoniacal. When
fully developed it resembles an enormous gramophone record
whirling madly round its own axis while advancing across the
sea at twelve to twenty-four miles an hour. When the Galveston hurricane hit the coast, the anemometer showed a

wind speed of 139 m.p.h. for five minutes before it broke down. Shortly after that a tidal wave, fifteen feet high, broke across the embankments and destroyed 3600 houses, while a deluge of 2000 tons of rain water drowned 6000 people in a single day.

The name of the Atlantic rotating storm is derived from the Amerindian storm-god "Hurakan." In the Pacific it is called Typhoon, off the Australian coast Willy-Willy, and Cyclone, in the Indian Ocean. All these storms have the same origin, the formation of a whirling mass of air over the sea in the belts of the equatorial doldrums. There are two theories about their creation: the old one which explains them as a collision between warm and cool trade winds, and the modern one, which has more followers to-day, and is called the warm air theory. This theory is as follows.

Hurricanes are formed in the doldrum belts of tropical oceans most often during late summer and early autumn. At this season the surface of the sea has reached its maximum temperature (about 27–30° C.). Meanwhile the doldrum belts have shifted so far north of the equator that they are set into a whirling motion by the centrifugal power of the earth's rotation. The details are as follows:

First phase: The sun heats up large masses of moist, warm sea air (above the easily heated land mass of a tropical island for instance) which rises in columns as if drawn up a gigantic chimney.

Second phase: The rising air is replaced by cooler air at the bottom. The air is given a spiral motion by the rotation of the earth as it streams inwards (clockwise in the Northern and anti-clockwise in the Southern hemisphere).

Third phase: The rising air meets increasingly colder atmospheric layers, is cooled in turn and forms clouds and raindrops. This liberates more heat, which increases the rate of ascent.

Fourth phase: The liberated heat becomes the motive power of the hurricane, and more masses of air stream upward, up to a million tons a second.

Fifth phase: The spiral winds above the sea increase in velocity. They develop a high centrifugal force which keeps open the centre, or "eye," of the hurricane. While it may rain buckets in the neighbourhood of the spiral winds, the sun often shines in a calm, clear sky in the eye of the storm.

Sixth phase: The hurricane is fully formed. The horizontally spinning devil's wheel slowly increases the forward speed of its path across the sea.

Most Atlantic hurricanes arise about nine hundred miles

south-east of the Bahamas and begin moving westwards. After travelling a certain distance they are deflected on a parabolic course towards the East Coast of America, between Florida and New York. They frequently reach this destination and cause havoc in the coastal areas. Some hurricanes leave this path before meeting the coast. Some move westwards into the Caribbean and reach the mountains of Central America. Others wander eastwards, following the southern and western edges of the Atlantic high pressure area in a tighter parabolic curve, to die out somewhere above the sea.

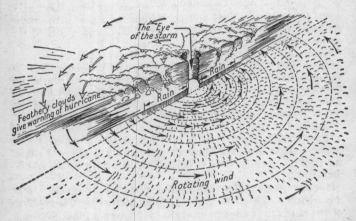

A hurricane is shaped like a gigantic gramophone record; constantly revolving round itself it moves across the sea. This cross-section shows the center or "eye" of the storm as well as the spirally arranged clouds, the wind directions and the rain zones.

It may happen that a hurricane deviates into the middle latitudes, turning into a normal low pressure storm area, to be carried across the North Atlantic as far as Europe by the west winds. Such a blunted hurricane passed the coast of North Germany early in 1953, giving the inhabitants a mild demonstration of its power.

A hurricane usually has a diameter of fifty to eight hundred miles, lasts from nine to twenty-five days, can cover a distance of up to 1800 miles and move many million tons of air. The greatest wind speeds are generated in a ring-shaped zone around the centre, where velocities of up to 180 miles per hour have been measured (Mount Washington Observatory, 1938). On the high seas the wind tears off the tops of the waves, drives them through the air in swathes, shreds them into pieces and carries the drops along horizontally. An eye-witness of the hurricane which hit the North American coast in 1938 wrote the following: "Over large areas the trees were flattened like matches. Houses were squashed as if a steam-roller had passed over them. A two-storey house in the neigh-bourhood of Madison, Connecticut, was blown a distance of over 2000 feet."

The first European known to have made the acquaintance of a hurricane was Columbus. When he crossed the Carib-bean in 1494 his ships had to seek shelter on the leeward side of an island to escape destruction by a violent storm. In the following year a hurricane destroyed three of his ships.

One of the most disastrous tropical whirlwinds of modern times reached Japan on 26th–27th September, 1954, in the form of the typhoon "Marie." One thousand seven hundred people died, more than 600 ships were sunk, 99,000 Japanese were rendered homeless and 20,000 buildings destroyed.

At the beginning of 1956 the typhoon "Emma" caused great damage in the Philippines and Japan. Its circular base was so large that it would have reached from London to Dundee if it had been transplanted to Britain. A month before that, one of the heaviest typhoons to hit North China since the beginning of the century killed nearly 2000 peo-ple, ruined half the cotton crop and destroyed 83,000 dwellings.

It is difficult to imagine the gruesome reality behind these cold figures. Our imagination shrinks from the pain and misery caused by these catastrophes. This is true of the sinking of the *Pamir*, the proud German sailing ship which was used as a training vessel. On the 21st of September, 1957, it ran into the hurricane "Carrie" near the Azores. The storm smashed the rigging, then it broke the hull and finally it pushed the ship under the waves with titanic force. Of the crew of nearly one hundred only a handful of young men were saved.

Since a hurricane needs both heat and moisture, it can only form and remain in motion over a large sea area and dies quickly once it reaches land. One of its most feared accom-paniments is the tidal wave, which is created by a process that never varies. The warm ascending air in the central vortex leaves a strong low pressure area at sea-level. At this spot the sea can be compared to a stretched piece of toy-balloon which a boy is sucking into his open mouth. The rubber curves inwards, and the sea behaves in a similar manner. The rising air lifts about two million tons of air from each square mile of surface, the air pressure decreases and the sea rises into a hill of water about ten feet high. When the storm moves forwards the hill of water follows, and helped by the wind and the waves it may occasionally reach a height of over twenty-five feet. The worst tidal waves are those which are blown into a V-shaped bay which compresses the waters and makes them even more dangerous. On the 7th of October, 1737, a cyclone in the Bay of Bengal drove a tidal wave, 40 feet high, towards the coast, destroying 20,000 ships of various sizes according to reliable reports, killing 250,000 people in Lower Bengal, wrecking huts and houses and flooding an area of the Ganges delta equal almost to that of Wales. Eye-witnesses have reported that the sea at first drew back as if preparing for its dreadful work, only to return with a devastating flood-wave.

Hurricanes sometimes beget swarms of hose-shaped air vortices on their edges but their most curious feature is the eye, the normally circular centre of the storm around which the spiral winds perform their satanic dance. The central zone is usually ten to twenty miles wide, and in this area the sea is comparatively calm, while a blue sky and a shining sun may even be seen above it. Some sea captains who have reached the eye of a hurricane remained in it by clever navigation until the storm blew itself out. An aeroplane pilot of the United States Navy once saw a sailing ship in the centre of a hurricane, and on it the crew were happily sunbathing, while around it all Hell was let loose. The eye is an oasis for all living creatures which stray into a hurricane. Sea-birds which are driven into the centre by the spiral winds are so exhausted that they settle on any ship they can reach. Mariners have told of ships which became packed with weather-beaten birds and insects. Despite the roaring winds all around the animals feel safe in the eye of the storm, and quite unconcerned they wait in the rigging for the end of the gale. If it survived the journey, a ship travelling in a straight line from the outer edge to the eye would pass from a region of comparatively high air pressure into zones of gradually decreasing pressure. The central vortex is the nucleus of the Low, where the barometer can sink to 880 millibars, recording values more than ten per cent lower than at the edge of the storm. Passengers relate that these low pressures strained their eardrums and brought a taste of blood to their mouths.

To prevent devastation the United States has, during the last ten years or so, developed an ingenious storm warning system in the West Atlantic (the most dangerous area). Since hurricanes are formed over the sea, the first warning usually comes from a ship. The captain sends a message to the U.S. Hurricane Centre in Miami, Florida. Miami notifies several aerodromes in Florida, Bermuda, Puerto Rico, etc., on which squadrons of so-called "weather flights" are stationed. A special aeroplane, fitted out as a kind of flying meteorological laboratory and carrying a crew of several men, usually starts out from the aerodrome nearest the hurricane. The target of the flight is the hurricane and the determination of its strength, direction and speed, so that areas in its probable path can be warned. When the characteristic spiral rainclouds first become visible on the radar screen at a distance of 250 miles, the hurricane is given a name. Despite the protests of American Women's Clubs, the Weather Bureau decided on feminine Christian names. The first hurricane of the season gets a name beginning with A, such as Alice, the second starts with B, and after that C, D and so on, so that no confusion can arise.

It is the dangerous duty of these pilots to fly around the hurricane in an anti-clockwise direction, gradually making their way into the interior, while taking continuous readings, until they reach the eye of the storm. This last dramatic piece of bravura is best achieved over the south-west portion of the spiral, where the winds are not quite so fierce. Once in the centre the meteorologist drops an automatic instrument to the surface of the sea by parachute. This apparatus periodically sends back information about humidity, air pressure and temperature through a small radio transmitter. From these figures the crew can calculate the direction and strength of the storm and they pass on this information to Miami which warns such coastal areas as are in danger.

Captain Augsburger, the leader of the squadron in Kindley, Bermuda, once said of these expeditions that they were a flight into hell, of which no one knew whether he would live through it. The winds pull and tear at the machine, the rain whips against the cabin and at times any reasonable navigation is impossible. It is a severe test for a pilot to carry on under such conditions, let alone carry out exact measurements. These flights are essential, however, for a hurricane of known strength and direction loses half its danger. Two examples can illustrate this best. In September 1928 a hurricane caused 1836 deaths in Florida. Only two lives were lost when a hurricane of equal strength hit the same area after a previous warning on the 4th of August, 1948. The 1926 hurricane in Miami caused 75 million dollars worth of

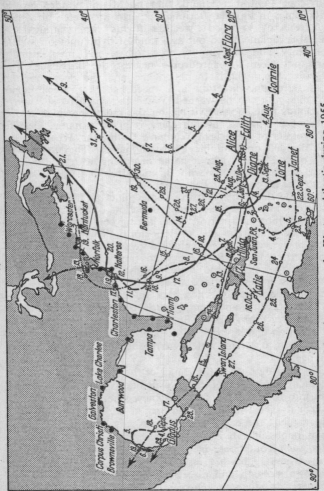

Tracks of hurricanes over the Western Atlantic during 1955.

damage, but a similar storm, which had been recognised in time, cost the State only 14 million dollars in 1950.

Recently American meteorologists have begun to use the curious behaviour of the water in the centre of the storm for determining its direction. Since the water in the centre of the hurricane rises to form a hill (as described previously) the pressure of the water on the sea bed below it is increased. As the storm moves forward the hill of water does as well, and the shift of water pressure can be detected by delicate seismographs (instruments for measuring earthquakes). If two or more seismographs in different coastal towns work in conjunction, the path of a hurricane can sometimes be found more accurately, and certainly with far less danger, than by weather flights.

The heavy loss of life, the many wounded and the substantial damage caused annually by hurricanes justify the massive use of modern scientific apparatus, men and materials. Only if we uncover the secrets of the storm and find out more and more about it, can we hope to combat it effectively some day.

Our map shows the paths of hurricanes during 1955, of which "Hilda" and "Janet" caused most loss of life. The dates are those on which observations were made. The black spots are radar Weather Stations that are either planned or already in use, tracking the hurricane paths. Small dots with circles around them show the position of radar weather stations for the hurricane research programme of 1956. This project required a dozen additional radar stations in the Lesser Antilles, Bahamas, Cuba and Jamaica as well as the weather pilots. In front of the East Coast of America hurricane buoys send automatic weather reports during the storm season (July to October). Rockets with automatic cameras photograph the wandering storms from an aerial perspective. If an Atlantic hurricane follows the normal route, it must pass these stations and cannot avoid having its pulse and temperature constantly taken. Even if it does finally hit the coast, it will in the meantime have yielded many of the secrets of its anatomy. By this means the Weather Service hopes to come closer to its goal: either to stifle this most fearful of storms at birth, or, if it should make its way towards the coast, to deflect it out to sea where it can work off its energy without causing damage.

Several attempts to achieve this result are already under way. Many American experts, for instance, hope for success by seeding the hurricane clouds in a manner similar to that employed when making rain from cumulus clouds. The hurricane is to be dusted with "dry ice" from an aeroplane or a radio-controlled rocket. In this way foci of crystallisation are introduced into the clouds, leading to the formation of ice particles. The theory is that the more and the larger the ice granules are, the easier they will fall down to melt in the warmer air below the clouds and turn into cloudbursts, thus robbing the storm of its power. Another idea is to set fire to large patches of oil on the sea. The hot, rising air is supposed to disturb the system of the hurricane and diffuse its strength. But the practicability of such experiments is still very much in doubt. So far it sounds rather like trying to kill an elephant with a pea-shooter.

15

THE JET-STREAM

OF ALL THE GALES AND STORMS ON THIS PLANET, man has only been able to subjugate, or rather make use of, a single one. Flyers call this wind the "gulf stream of the air," because its typical shape is that of a tube stretching across the sky. It is called the jet-stream, and its discovery resembles an adventure story.

On a sunny day in 1944 a long-distance American B.29 bomber droned across the Pacific Ocean. The crew, experienced, reliable airmen, were briefed to attack a target in Japan. The weather forecast had promised good flight conditions and nothing seemed to stand in their way.

As they left the mainland a feeling of anxiety gripped the pilot and spread to the whole crew. At first they believed that their senses deceived them, but their doubts soon vanished, for something was definitely holding their machine back. An invisible hand seemed to be tugging at the stern of the aeroplane and, although all the engines were at full throttle, the B.29 was only moving forwards with difficulty. A group of islands that they had passed quickly on previous flights remained in their field of vision for an exceptionally long time; finally the bomber almost stood still in the air.

What had happened? The B.29 had flown into a jet-stream, one of those treacherous tube-shaped air zones in which the wind blows from west to east at tremendous speeds. The bomber's engines fought in vain against this hurricane-like storm of the upper air. The pilot did not reach his target that day, but had to return home after dropping his load of bombs harmlessly into the sea.

Whilst the United States Air Force was having its first experience of the jet-stream, the Japanese already had some knowledge of these mysterious currents. They knew, for instance, that a fairly constant high wind blew from their islands to the American West Coast, and they even made use of it during the last months of the war. Under the direction of General Kusaba, Japanese technicians constructed special balloons, which were intended to set fire to the American forests, after being carried over the ocean by the jet-stream.

No less than 9000 balloons started out for the American West Coast during the "balloon offensive" in the spring of 1944 and winter 1944–45. It was a major offensive, if one considers that each balloon cost about £ 200, and it was also a major technical achievement. During the flight of about 2500 miles an ingenious mechanism kept the balloons at a height between 29,000 and 36,000 feet, just where the meteorologists had found the jet-stream. The control of height was cleverly managed: a barometer worked the release which dropped one of thirty little sandbags whenever the balloon sank below 29,000 feet. If it rose higher than 36,000 feet, a valve released some of the hydrogen which lifted the balloon. Accompanying control balloons carried short-wave equipment, and sent back reports on their position at certain intervals, so that the whereabouts of the flotilla could be checked.

We know now that only about nine hundred balloons (or ten per cent) reached the American mainland between Mexico and Alaska. Some of them landed in coastal waters, some of them drifted two hundred and fifty miles inland; some exploded and some started fires, but they caused little damage. The Japanese venture was soon forgotten, but the jet-streams were not, and their importance in modern aerial communications is constantly growing. They have already become what the trade winds once were for sailing ships, a gift from Nature which, correctly used, saves fuel and travelling time.

The riddle of the jet-streams pricked the curiosity of the meteorologists. They pondered the question how Nature manages to create a sudden suction in such a mobile medium as the air, and how it happens that they are narrow, sharply defined zones in which the air races along like a mountain torrent, carrying everything before it?

German meteorologists had already in the nineteen-thirties come across ribbons of exceptionally strong winds at a great height and called them "High Jet Currents," but the first steps toward their explanation were taken by a group of Chicago weather experts. The Americans had sent up balloons to heights where the jet-streams blew, collected reports from other countries and systematically worked towards an explanation. Gradually they built up a picture of the jet-streams which was at least as complete as our knowledge of other aerial conditions, such as those leading to thunderstorms.

It is a matter of fact that jet-streams occur at between 20,000 to 35,000 feet and that their height is greater in summer than in winter. They can attain the fantastic speed of 300 or even more than 370 miles per hour, and preferentially occur in zones of varying width, about 1800 miles from the equator, completely encircling both hemispheres of the globe.

The scientists got a pointer from the fact that the jet-streams occurred particularly in the middle latitudes and travelled mainly from west to east. From this they could deduce that they were perhaps connected with the distribution of temperature over the earth. This proved to be true; wherever the jet-streams blew, warm tropical air met cold polar air.

Let us take an example (see diagram) and imagine a High

Under certain conditions jet-streams are formed where warm and cold air masses meet. A typical jet-stream generating weather map over the Atlantic. Between the High *(below centre)* and the Low *(over Iceland)* masses of warm *W* and cold *C* air meet.

over the Azores in the Atlantic and two Lows to the west and east of it. Above Iceland in the north there is the centre of another strong Low, which on its part is flanked by Highs on the west (Canada) and east (North Scandinavia). Under such conditions, which are by no means rare, warm air will stream north-east from the edge of the High over the Azores and cold air will flow south-west from the edge of the Low over Iceland. The two air streams will meet approximately over the fiftieth degree of latitude to form a weather-front, a region of marked differences of temperature.

The birth place of the jet-stream winds lies in this weather-front at a height of about six miles. Every weather expert knows that there is a strong pressure difference between cold air and warm air at great heights. The air, like any other gas, tries to eliminate this difference and begins to move from the warm to the cold side. If the temperature differential is very great, this movement becomes violent. It is as if two canals ran along a sloping hillside at different heights; if the upper one overflows, the water will run down the hill and collect in the lower one just like the air on its journey from the warm region (South) to the cold region (North). There is one difference, however: whereas the water will flow from one canal to the other in a direct line, the air that was originally moving from south to north will be deflected by the earth's rotation. If we are in the Northern Hemisphere it will be deflected to the right and the final direction will therefore be from west to east; the jet-stream is born.

The hotter the warm air and the cooler the cold air, the greater will be the pressure difference in high regions. The greater this difference, the greater will be the speed of the jet-stream, which has the strongest turbulence in the centre and less violent winds at its edges.

It is of great importance for a pilot to ascertain quickly if there is a jet-stream in the vicinity of his route, and whether he can count on strong and steady winds. An experienced pilot can often recognise a jet-stream by the typical clouds which accompany it. To the south of it there is usually a layer of feathery, riffled or striated cirrus cloud which runs parallel to the stream and often extends from one end of the horizon to the other. To the north the sky is usually clear and deep-blue, while there is often a bank of lenticularis alto-cumulus clouds below the jet-stream itself (these clouds are the same as those seen over mountain peaks during a Föhn, when they glisten in the sun like small pennants of smoke). It is not always possible to make a long-distance diagnosis, however, for sometimes jet-streams occur mysteriously in a clear sky.

If the pilot does not want to trust to luck in his search, he has another method as well, temperature measurement. The temperature is distributed around the jet-stream according to certain laws, and a knowledge of these laws will turn the thermometer into a sort of Geiger-counter. With a little ingenuity the pilot can tell from temperature readings whether he is to the north or south, above or below the jet-stream.

Once the pilot is inside the jet-stream he must navigate carefully so as not to lose it. Modern technology has called in radar, the new "maid-of-all-work," and given the pilot an instrument on which he can read the direction and speed of the stream right away.

The importance of always knowing the exact direction of this moody wind is demonstrated by an ominous fact. It may happen that the jet-stream is forced from its path by a sudden advance of cold polar air, in which case "squall-zones" may appear in its immediate neighbourhood. These are regions in which the strength of the wind varies, exposing the aeroplane to dangerously changing loads.

Such squall zones probably played an important part in the incompletely understood disaster of the Comet, the British jet plane which was lost over the Mediterranean on the 10th of January, 1954. A glance at the diagram below will show you the air pressure distribution high over Europe on the day of the accident. The lines, which connect points of equal air pressure, show a distinct concentration over Western Europe. A meteorologist will deduce a strong hurricane band running from high over the North Atlantic via Western Germany and the Western Mediterranean to the North African coast, where it bends eastwards. The jet-stream itself, however, was not the main danger. The decisive point was that warm tropical air (high pressure areas marked H on the left of the map) was pushing from the west to the north-east on the western and eastern side of a sack-shaped wedge of cold air. This led to a squall zone between Rome and Sardinia at a height of about six miles, well within the route of the Comet, which mysteriously disintegrated.

He who wants to "ride the high storm" must be aware of the dangers and know how to avoid them. If this is the case he can go hunting for records, trying to lower the times for long, trans-oceanic flights. Aeroplanes flying from Tokyo to the United States in the jet-stream have already saved about six hours' flying time, and over two thousand gallons of fuel. The American pilot R. P. McManus took a passenger plane from Tokyo to Anchorage (Alaska) in 9 hours and

19 minutes, and this included a stop at the island of Shemya in the Aleutians.

Flights of an equally impressive nature are also possible across the Atlantic and the European mainland, for the ribbon of the jet-stream stretches right round the globe like a meandering river: from the Himalayas via Japan to North America, onward across the Atlantic to Europe and back to

Was it the fault of the weather?

This map shows the distribution of air pressure over Europe on 10th January, 1954. The weather expert can deduce from it that a jet-stream blew across the Western Mediterranean at a time when the Comet, a British jet plane, met with an accident in that region. In addition to this there was also a "squall-zone."

Asia. As flying techniques improve the thrust of the jet-stream will be used increasingly, and the feats which only a few pilots can manage to-day will become a routine job for all to-morrow. Perhaps the factories will turn out aeroplanes which can ride the storm with unpowered flight. This would be an event of which we could say that the dream of the flying carpet has come true.

16

THUNDER AND LIGHTNING

BETWEEN WERRA AND FULDA, in Central Germany, lies a range of mountains, the Rhön, which recalls wonderful gliding contests, effortless flight across fields and meadows and the marvellous "thermals," currents of rapidly rising air which can carry the glider to endless heights. During favourable weather the Rhön is a veritable glider's paradise, but on a close summer day in 1938 high above the hillside a tragic misadventure occurred.

Another contest had been announced. Enthusiastic competitors arrived with their streamlined "birds" of all colours and types. The slightly thundery atmosphere gave promise of record-breaking attempts, and in fact heights of over 26,000 feet were reached in several cases. Then five daring contestants flew into a thunder cloud.

It is possible that they did not correctly read the danger in the cloud's appearance, or that they were carried away by the spirit of competition and got too close. All five of them were suddenly sucked into the centre of a violent squall. It jerked the gliders upward and the dense cloud blotted out all visibility. Fearing they would be thrown against a cliff, or perhaps because their gliders were already damaged, the flyers jumped and pulled the release cord of their parachutes.

The consequences were dreadful. Instead of falling gently downwards the parachutes were filled to bursting point by the wind and carried upwards. Higher and higher they soared into increasingly colder layers of the cloud. However hard they tried to steer with their arms and legs they could not escape the howling force of the gale. Huge raindrops soaked their bodies in a few seconds. Hailstones lashed their faces. It was as if nature were punishing this audacious handful of men for venturing into forbidden heights.

We do not know all that happened between earth and sky during these frightful minutes, as only one man, severely injured, escaped with his life. We can only imagine the ordeal of the other four. At a height of thirty-five, forty-five or even fifty thousand feet they must have been enclosed in a casing of frozen water, tossed about like living icicles, stabbed at by lightning, until the cloud released their four lifeless bodies.

Nothing could demonstrate more clearly the forces at work inside a thundercloud than this accident in the Rhön. They resemble a titanic grapple between cold and warm air. It is their collision, only partly visible from the ground, and all its attendant phenomena that we call a "thunderstorm."

In the meteorologist's language a thunderstorm is "a local storm accompanied by lightning, thunder, and often by strong gusts of wind, heavy rain, and sometimes hail . . . frequently [having] its beginnings in unstable moist air which gives rise to strong convectional currents and the development of cumulo-nimbus clouds." The sixteen million thunderstorms that occur all over the globe during one year can be divided into two basic types. The "heat" thunderstorms which are caused by rising, moist, warm air and frontal thunderstorms which are due to a large wedge of cold air undercutting and lifting warmer air. Whereas heat thunderstorms occur almost exclusively in summer and are localised over the mainland, frontal thunderstorms may be met in winter and at sea. Several often occur along the edge of an advancing cold front (line-squall zone). In Germany, for instance, a whole barrage of thunderstorms may move eastwards along a front between the North Sea and the Alps. The line-squall front displaces the warm air and is followed by cold air.

To produce a thunderstorm two conditions must be fulfilled: the rising air must contain sufficient humidity to supply the growing thundercloud with moisture and the temperature must fall rapidly with increasing height. Such conditions are more frequent in equatorial regions than in the higher latitudes. In the moist tropics there are 80 to 160 days of heat thunderstorms annually, in Central Europe only 15 to 25 days. The town which suffers most is probably Buitenzorg on Java, where there is thunder and lightning (on an average) 322 days of the year.

During the course of a few cloudless summer days it is interesting to watch how the sun warms up the air layers near the ground and at the same time sucks up moisture. When this process has reached a certain stage, small clouds appear in the sky, as a sign that the rising moisture has been condensed at a great height. On the next day the cloud formation is denser and finally the characteristic cumulo-nimbus clouds, which can swell up to a height of 26,000 feet or more, are formed, often over a hill or mountain peak. High above the cauliflower-shaped cloud there is a mighty crown made up of billions of fine ice crystals. This is the "cirrus umbrella" of the thundercloud, and it often takes on the shape of a gigantic white anvil.

The fully formed thundercloud exhibits a series of intri-

cate processes, the elucidation of which has been the target
of a team of American meteorologists since the Second
World War. Led by Professor H. R. Byers their research has
resulted in a mass of information, so that our present day
knowledge about the formation and course of a thunderstorm is fairly extensive.

One important discovery from this investigation was that
a thunderstorm is invariably developed from a sort of single
nucleus or mother cell (the original cumulus cloud). This
mother cell, according to Byers, multiplies by forming daugh-
ter cells (rather like the reproduction of certain bacteria),
which in their turn go through a mature and dissipating
stage, propagating the thunderstorm through the air, so to
speak, in a series of jumps.

Let us look at what happens in the interior of a thundercloud. There is an upward stream of air which rises at about
100 feet a second, almost equivalent to wind force twelve.
This stream, the so-called "chimney-current," is only about
thirty feet wide. It carries warm, moisture-laden air upwards, and as this cools rapid condensation and the formation of drops of water takes place. The cloud swells, new
growths bulge out of its sides, and at the same time the
formation of drops generates heat and reinforces the rising
wind.

It is not surprising that the droplets coalesce under such
stormy conditions, thus becoming heavier and tending to
fall downwards. The upwind inside the cloud is too powerful, however, and continues to whirl them upwards. Large
and small drops are carried to the ice-cold upper regions of
the cloud where they freeze to hailstones. At a height of
20,000 to 25,000 feet above the surface the strength of the
chimney current is finally exhausted. The ice-granules, which
have danced on it like celluloid balls on jets of water, can
disperse in all directions and millions of them fall down outside the chimney. They in turn carry air with them, so that
there is a vigorous downward movement of cold air. Now it
is only a question of time before the descending winds hit
the earth's surface and cause violent cloudbursts and hailstorms. A historic case illustrates the havoc such storms can
cause. In April 1360 the English army under King Edward
III lost so many men and horses in a hailstorm outside Paris
that the king signed the Peace of Brétigny.

"If there is lightning then it's a thunderstorm" is a saying
which concisely states one of the essentials, namely, that the
electric discharge and a thunderstorm go together, much as
summer weather and blue skies. Since primitive times lightning has been a climactic point in the celestial drama. The

ancient Teutons said it was the hammer of Thor, the God of Thunder, which he angrily flung at the earth, and the Greeks that it was the flaming spears which Zeus, the father of the Gods, hurled down from the skies.

The American philosopher and inventor, Benjamin Franklin (1706–90), had already recognised the true nature of lightning. He said that the bright streaks in the sky were a form of electricity, a subject about which little was known in his age. Franklin undertook to verify his theory in 1752 by a simple but dangerous experiment. He sent up a kite as a lightning conductor during a thunderstorm and tied a key to the end of the string. The key gave off sparks and Franklin was thoroughly satisfied with the success of his experiment. He did not realise how close he had been to death. A year later similar ignorance produced a less fortunate result. Inspired by Franklin's kite an eminent member of the St. Petersburg Academy of Science, Dr. Richmann, put a lightning conductor on his house. He chose a bar of iron for this purpose, and for some reason led it through the roof so that it ended just above his desk. During a thunderstorm a stroke of lightning hit the bar and killed him instantaneously.

Meteorologists to-day are more careful when they try to find out the extent of the electrical charges in a thundercloud. During the American "thunderstorm project" of 1946–49 special balloons were sent into different parts of thunderclouds and automatically sent their observations back to earth. Aeroplane pilots photographed cumulo-nimbus clouds from all directions and radar apparatus determined the size of water droplets and ice granules inside them. The results did not give a complete picture, but they did provide many valuable pointers.

We know that lightning is an enormous electric spark which neutralises electrical charges. Before it can flash, areas

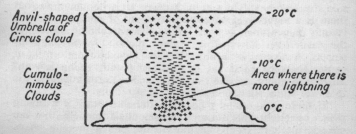

A thunder-cloud in cross-section. Positively charged areas of cloud above and below, negatively charged areas in the centre.

of opposing electric charges must be created inside the cloud. How does that come about?

Most theories agree that a cloud contains positive and negative electricity before it becomes charged. The strong winds separate the two types of electricity so that areas of positive and negative charge are created inside the cloud. The mechanism of the separation of the charges is extremely complicated and it is probable that several independent processes are involved. One of these is most likely the cold air descending. The large raindrops inside it are partially captured by ascending squalls in the lower layers of the clouds; that is, small portions are torn off the edges and carried upward again, while the main bulk keeps on falling. Experiments in the laboratory indicate that the small torn-off droplets become negatively charged, while the main bulk remains positive. A similar phenomenon occurs when the ice granules in the uppermost parts of the clouds split into pieces; the parts carrying negative charges move towards the centre while those with positive charges remain above. All these processes are much too complicated to be described in a few words, but the final outcome is that the upper and lower zones of the clouds are enriched with positive electricity, while the centre becomes negatively charged. As soon as the charges are strong enough the lightning can begin to flash.

This means that the lightning is created inside the cloud and in general also neutralises the charges inside it. The widely held belief that it releases the enormous potential between the clouds (positive pole) and the earth (negative pole) has been proved to be erroneous. Laboratory experiments have shown repeatedly that most lightning flashes originate at the boundary between the lower positive and central negative areas of a thundercloud. The starting point is always a single droplet or ice crystal from which two tiny sparks travel upwards and downwards. How these sparks grow with "lightning speed" is still not fully known. It is certain, however, that they move spasmodically into areas of opposite charges. While they branch out the charged areas above and below give way like snow before a snow plough. In this way the sparks always have strong electric fields in front of them, and the discharge grows at fantastic speed. Frequently the discharge jumps outside the cloud and makes its way to the ground. The earth is struck by lightning.

Lightning flashes in a heat thunderstorm have a width of one to twelve inches on an average. Their luminous track is created by air particles in the vicinity which become white-hot and reach temperatures of up to 30,000° C.

In Germany lightning generally develops a current strength

of between 10,000 and 20,000 amperes, but giant flashes of over 100,000 amperes also occur, particularly in North America. Despite these enormous quantities the technical utilisation of lightning would not be practicable because of its extremely short duration of about 1/1000th of a second.

Discharges which do not reach the earth but remain inside the cloud cause the glow of sheet lightning which may last for several seconds. A different sort of discharge, which leaves the cloud but is only seen as glow in the sky because intervening obstacles prevent direct observation, is called summer lightning.

Most of the flashes which we see during a thunderstorm are of the well known forked or line discharge type, but there are other forms, some of which are most peculiar. Among these are the rare string-of-beads and ball lightning. The string-of-beads lightning seems to be an ordinary flash which has been divided into a series of shining, spherical balls which have an afterglow of one, two or three seconds. The distance between the beads is always the same, twenty-five to forty feet. A ball of lightning is probably nothing but a bead which has fallen out of the string. Such glowing individual balls can sometimes develop an eerie life of their own. It is related that a ball of lightning entered a room in which a girl was sitting at a table, travelled around her in a spiral, escaped up the chimney and exploded on the roof with a loud detonation. Other reports, which can be taken more seriously, indicate that the ball can reach a diameter of several yards but is frequently only as large as an egg. They are said to be able to remain stationary or to travel at several yards a second. They can remain in the air for several minutes and are even reported to have slipped through keyholes. They frequently give off an asphyxiating, acrid odour. Professor Toepler, the well-known lightning specialist, describes ball lightning as completely silent and normally harmless, since its current strength is usually below one ampere. The "final bang" of some of them is due to a line discharge with which they end in such cases.

Signs that lightning is imminent are sometimes seen on the rigging of ships, house-corners and the ice-picks of mountaineers. When the air is strongly charged small, blue lights lick around such objects. This is St. Elmo's fire, named after the patron saint of Mediterranean sailors, an Italian bishop who took office around A.D. 300 and who was famous for his extreme goodness and piety. St. Elmo's fire itself is fairly harmless, but under certain circumstances it can set fire to easily inflammable gases. The "Hindenburg" was probably set alight thus after its Atlantic crossing on the 6th of May,

1937. It caught fire at the Lakehurst aerodrome in America after the hydrogen from a damaged container had mingled with oxygen from the air to form a dangerously explosive mixture.

Now that we have described the causes and forms of lightning, we can turn to its audible companion, the thunder.

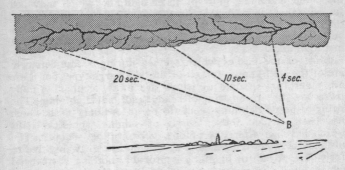

Fig. 1

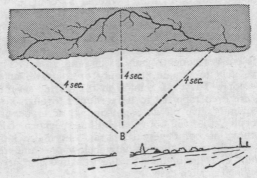

Fig. 2

We know that thunder is created when a flash of lightning expands explosively along its discharge track. The sudden thrust is transmitted as a detonation wave. When the lightning strikes less than 150 feet from the observer the thunder crack sounds like breaking wood or sometimes like the slap of a whip lash. With increasing distance its voice becomes lower until, at ten or twelve miles, it only sounds like a hollow rumble.

The reason why thunder keeps on grumbling for some time after the stroke of lightning is very simple; in such cases the sound waves from a discharge reach the observer at different times. An example of this is given in Figure 1. If, on the other hand, the discharge is immediately above the observer at B (Figure 2) so that all the sound waves reach him at once, the clap of thunder is of shorter duration but greater intensity.

There are innumerable instances of lightning killing men and animals, setting fire to houses, ships and fields, splitting tree trunks, damaging huts and causing hundreds of other kinds of damage. The large amount of destruction is partly due to the enormous numbers of lightning flashes which reach the earth. During the ten seconds or so which you have spent reading this paragraph about one thousand streaks of lightning have hit the earth. Only a very small proportion of them will have harmful consequences, but a few figures and examples will illustrate the potential danger of lightning.

On an average one man a day is killed by lightning in the United States alone, and four people are injured, mainly anglers, hunters, people on holiday and farmers. The annual damage amounts to about twelve million dollars. In Germany two to four people per million inhabitants are killed by lightning every year, usually through their own carelessness. In England the annual figure is twenty and in Switzerland five or six. The greatest number of lightning flashes hits us in July, the month with the most thunderstorms in the year. Lightning preferably strikes solitary trees, metallic objects, mountain tops and groups of people in open fields.

Lightning also shows a strong tendency to hit isolated farms, churches, mills and wooden ships at sea. (The English meteorologist C. Botley has calculated that between 1810 and 1815 no less than fifty-eight wooden sailing ships were struck by lightning, and some of them severely damaged.) On the 22nd of June, 1918, lightning struck a flock of sheep in the Wasatch National Forest (Utah). The animals had crowded together in an open space and this one stroke killed 504 of them.

Lightning is capricious and unpredictable, and can have the most curious consequences. On one occasion it set fire to a house and went on to strike the adjacent fire alarm, calling the fire brigade to its own handiwork. F. W. Lane tells of a lady whose ear-rings were melted by lightning and Flammarion speaks of a murderer in Kentucky who was struck by lightning at the very moment he stepped on to the scaffold. In Virginia lightning is said to have set a railway signal at "all clear" and caused two trains to collide. There are also impressive examples of the power of lightning. Probably the strongest flash of lightning ever to be measured hit the "Cathedral of Learning" at the University of Pittsburgh on the 31st of July, 1947. The strength of its current would have been sufficient to light up 600,000 electric bulbs of sixty watts each as long as it was in the air.

There are a number of ways of avoiding being struck by lightning, if you follow certain rules. The old German adage "avoid oaks and seek beeches" is a good guide if you are caught out in the open. If there are no woods in the neighbourhood (they are safer than open country) a cave or projecting rock will do as shelter. In general valleys are less often struck by lightning than hills or mountain tops. Wet clothes conduct lightning to the ground better than dry ones, therefore it is better not to carry an umbrella and get wet if there is no chance of getting shelter. Metal objects always should be treated with care. Staying in the water is dangerous and under no circumstances should a bath or shower be taken during a thunderstorm, since the metal parts are good conductors.

Death can result from being struck by lightning, but sometimes it only produces "pictures" on the skin which look like tattoos of trees. The air pressure can cause asthmatic symptoms, and the lightning itself can produce effects on the nervous system, unconsciousness, burns and damage to the inner organs. The treatment for affected persons is identical to that for electric shock: heart massage and artificial respiration; and the golden rule is to *keep on,* for it has been known that apparently dead people have been revived after three hours of systematic treatment.

PART THREE

17

GAS CYCLES

OXYGEN IS ONLY THE SECOND MOST COMMON GAS IN THE AIR (nitrogen comprises nearly eighty per cent of the atmosphere), but taking the earth as a whole it is the commonest element by far. In different forms, it accounts for nearly a fifth of the air, about one-half of the earth's crust and almost nine-tenths of all water. In the crust of the earth oxygen is usually bound to metals, in water it is combined with hydrogen and only in the air does it appear in its pure, gaseous form. In the atmosphere it exists as a teeming mass of mobile molecules consisting of two atoms of oxygen (O_2), or of three atoms O_3) in the ozone layer.

Chemists say that oxygen is one of the most active or dynamic elements. This means that it has a distinct tendency to combine with other substances, except the rare gases and noble metals. We have only to look out of the window to see that oxygen plays a part in nearly all the processes around us. Plants, animals and men need it for respiration, indeed all living things depend upon it. All engines that burn petrol need it, so that it helps to drive cars, aeroplanes and outboard motors. Since coal and oil could not burn without oxygen locomotives and ocean-going liners require it in order to move. It maintains the flames of the gas fire and of the candle on our birthday cake. If we tried to keep it away from all these things, life would become very difficult: cars would stop, aeroplanes crash to earth, boats wallow helplessly on the waves.

In certain other circumstances oxygen is anything but beneficial, in fact we do our utmost to avoid it. Metal objects, for instance, are often covered with grease or protective paint to keep the air away, because metal is often attacked by the oxygen in moist air. Iron soon becomes covered with the ugly red coating that we call rust.

The process of rusting gives us a good example of the activity of oxygen. Just as it can combine with substances which burn or glow to give flames, heat and light (or even explosions as in the case of gunpowder), it can also combine with

iron. The process of rusting is simply slower and less noticeable, so that weeks or even months may pass before the rust
becomes apparent.

The combination of oxygen with other substances is called
oxidation and many of the products of this process are called
oxides. The expression was coined by the French chemist
Lavoisier who also gave the gas its Latin name. He called it
oxygenium, meaning "the acid maker," in the erroneous belief that all acids contain oxygen and that this was one of
their most important characteristics. Rusting is a type of oxidation and there are many similar biological changes inside
living creatures who obtain energy in the form of warmth by
this method. Finally, oxygen also participates in the decomposition of dead organisms.

To obtain oxygen in a pure form, you can carry out the
following experiment. Place about two fluid ounces of a three
per cent hydrogen peroxide solution (which you can buy at
any chemist's shop) in a large glass vessel. If you now sprin-
kle about a teaspoonful of manganese dioxide into it, a
colourless, odourless and tasteless gas is given off, which is
shown to be oxygen by a classical method. If you lead the
gas through a piece of rubber tubing into the bottom end of
a cylinder (which is closed at the top) and place a glowing
splint inside the cylinder, the splint will burst into flame
because of the combustion-supporting power of the oxygen.
If you want to be more exact you can first fill the cylinder
with water and place it with the opening downwards inside
a bowl of water. If you now place the end of the rubber tubing below the surface of the water and inside the bottom of
the cylinder, bubbles of gas will rise and slowly fill the cylinder with oxygen. In chemical terminology, two molecules of
hydrogen peroxide are split into two molecules of water and
one molecule of oxygen, which escapes in gaseous form:

$$2 \ H_2O_2 = 2 \ H_2O + O_2$$

Although it is the essential element, oxygen does not form
the larger part of the air we breathe. About four-fifths of
the atmosphere consists of nitrogen, an unreactive gas which
the chemists abbreviate as N (from Nitrogenium meaning
saltpetre or nitre-forming). The reason for Nitrogen's unreactive nature is that it normally consists of two atoms (N_2),
which in contrast to those composing oxygen (O_2) are very
happily married and spend most of their energy in sticking
together, so that they have little interest in other elements.
In our atmosphere the nitrogen acts as a sort of diluent for
the oxygen. All types of oxidation and decomposition would
be much more rapid if the nitrogen were absent, for it acts

as a chemical brake. Our respiration is one exception to this, but that will be dealt with in the next chapter.

Nitrogen can be obtained from the atmosphere by first making "liquid air" (cooling it at a certain pressure). Liquid air has a temperature of about −192° C. and is a clear, faintly blue fluid. Nitrogen is the first gas to evaporate, for its boiling point is −194° C., in other words it is already over-heated at −192° C. It can now be collected in suitable vessels and used for many purposes.

What part does nitrogen play in the economy of nature? Its most important role is to collaborate in making plant and animal proteins. All organisms require nitrogen in order to live. Unfortunately they cannot get it from the air as easily as one gets water from a tap, for, as we already said, nitrogen is a very unreactive element and will not always do what is wanted. In one respect this is just as well, for if it were as active as oxygen, it would combine with sea water to form the poisonous nitrous acid, the consequences of which would be unimaginable. On the other hand the inertness of nitrogen can prove inconvenient. To make it available to living organisms it has to be combined with other substances by complicated processes. Only in the form of nitrogen compounds does it become usable and digestible for plants and animals.

One method of turning nitrogen into a usable form is by electric discharges in the atmosphere which turn it into nitrates, but the amounts concerned are relatively small. The lion's share of the conversion of nitrogen is done by an army of tiny, but indispensable, organisms which live below the earth—the nitrogen-fixing bacteria. These helpful creatures either live free in the soil or in the roots of leguminous plants such as clover, beans, peas, lupins or alfalfa. They cause nodular growths in the roots of such plants, and are therefore also called "nodule bacteria." They help the plants to make a red pigment in the nodules, the so-called "leghæmoglobin" (a contraction of leguminous and hæmoglobin) which is similar to the red blood pigment of man. This pigment plays an important part in converting nitrogen into a form which is acceptable to the plant. The bacteria and the plant seem to co-operate in making leghæmoglobin, and once it is formed it probably converts the nitrogen into amino-acids by chemical means. The American scientists Lipman and Conybeare have calculated that five and a half million tons of nitrogen are transformed annually in the U.S.A. alone by the intimate co-operation of leguminous plants and the bacteria in their root nodules. This is more than twice all the nitrogenous fertiliser produced in one year by the whole world.

Added to this, there is the work of the free-living nitrogen-fixing bacteria. Together with the nodule bacteria they give the plants the nitrogen they require in a usable form (including ammonia) and fulfil a biological function which is at least as important as the assimilation of plants (see page 50 et seq.).

After a certain time the nitrogen returns to the air in its old form, as if it did not like its forced imprisonment inside living organisms. If one follows this remarkable gas through all its forms and changes, one can see that it undergoes a regular life-cycle in nature:

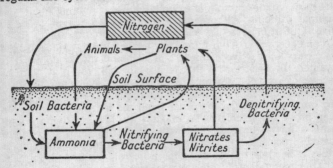

The nitrogen cycle in nature.

First process: Nitrogen is taken from the air by nitrogen-fixing bacteria in the soil and converted into forms which plants can use (ammonia, amino-acids, etc.).

Second process: Plants and animals use these nitrogen compounds to build up their own body substances.

Third process: When plants and animals die the nitrogen compounds in their body are decomposed to ammonia. The ammonia penetrates into the soil and is used again by living plants and animals.

Fourth process: A group of soil inhabitants called the "nitrifying bacteria," convert the ammonia into salts of nitric and nitrous acid (nitrates and nitrites). These substances can also be used by certain plants to build up body substances.

Fifth process: A third group of bacteria, called "denitrifying," break down the nitrates and nitrites into their components; this liberates nitrogen which can escape back into the air.

Since nitrogen is essential to the well-being of plants it is not surprising that people with a knowledge of agriculture thought of enriching the soil by artificial means with a form of nitrogen acceptable to the plants. The more nitrogen there is in the soil, they told themselves, the better our crops will grow and the higher will be the yields. The first person to give practical application to this idea was the German chemist Justus von Liebig. His book *Organic Chemistry and its Application in Agriculture and Physiology* appeared in 1840, and can be said to have founded the science of artificial fertilisation. Liebig's ideas encouraged experiments in laboratories and elsewhere, and chemists soon learned to produce nitrogen compounds which were useful fertilisers, such as ammonium sulphate, sodium nitrate, calcium cyanamide and urea.

These substances aid the growth and ripening of plants, as does Chile saltpetre, a natural ore which consists of nitrogen combined with sodium and oxygen. All of them, however, are only agricultural aids; the main work is still done by tiny bacteria in the earth, too small to be seen with the naked eye. The farmer therefore often resorts to a well-tried and ancient method of enriching the soil. Towards the end of the year he will plough under a crop of lupins or alfalfa, plants which possess the desired bacteria in their root nodules.

Carbon dioxide (CO_2), the third main component of the air, is created by all types of combustion. It also escapes from volcanoes in large quantities and is formed by the respiration of men, animals and plants. Despite these numerous sources it only amounts to 0.03 per cent of our atmosphere, and this is just as well, for experiments have shown that large amounts of this gas are dangerous to human beings. A man can inhale a concentration of up to one per cent carbon dioxide without any discomfort. If the concentration increases much above this level toxic symptoms begin to appear. At five to six per cent the rate of respiration accelerates and about eight per cent causes vertigo and giddiness. At nine per cent there is mortal danger, recognisable by the fact that a candle will stop burning. (This is why the "candle test" is used in places where there is danger of carbon dioxide poisoning, such as deep wells or disused mine shafts. Here the air does not move and carbon dioxide collects at the bottom because it is heavier than the other gases in the atmosphere).

Plants take up carbon dioxide and combine it with water with the aid of sunlight, turning it into sugar and starch. During the daytime this process, called "assimilation," is vigorous. Despite the small amount of carbon dioxide in the air the assimilation can outstrip the respiration of plants (i.e. taking in oxygen and giving off carbon dioxide). If human beings had this enviable power, and our skin was suffused with chlorophyll which was capable of assimilation, our nutritional problems could be solved very easily. All we would have to do would be to suck a few pastilles containing mineral salts, expose our bodies to the sunlight for a few hours and our appetites would be satisfied. Nature has not, however, developed us to this point. We are still dependent on food prepared (not to say predigested) for us by the plant and animal kingdoms. Men and animals are the last link in a circular chain, and their only task in this cycle is to return carbon dioxide into the atmosphere by their breath. This completes the circulation of the gas which is then again taken up by plants, transferred to animals and returned to the air, there to begin its cycle all over again.

18

RESPIRATION

Every living thing must breathe. Only those organisms that obtain their energy by fermentation can do without breath, and they belong to the most primitive, unicellular living beings. If the atmosphere were to escape into space, life would cease because the vital oxygen would no longer be available. Oxygen is even more essential to life than food and drink, for a man would inevitably die after being deprived of oxygen for fifteen minutes, whereas he can usually survive two days without water and three days without solid food.

What makes oxygen so essential? Why are we so dependent on it, and what happens to it inside our bodies?

One of the greatest discoveries of science was that all manifestations of life are based on combustion inside the tiny cells of the body. Just as in a stove or fire-place, the heat of this combustion inside us is the source of the energy which maintains life. Living cells burn fat and sugar molecules, which means that the molecules are destroyed with the aid of oxygen, and a modicum of warmth is liberated at the same time.

Nature had developed many methods of providing organisms with a sure and adequate supply of oxygen. Land plants have tiny openings on the under-surface of their leaves, microscopic air holes, which make respiration possible. Water plants usually absorb the oxygen dissolved in the water through their leaf surfaces. Botanists say that the respiratory gas diffuses into the plant; it moves (like a fluid) from a region of high concentration—the water—to a region of low concentration—the inside of the plant. After the cells have used the oxygen for combustion it is combined with carbon and excreted as carbon dioxide. This "respiration" is in direct contrast to "assimilation," during which green plants take up carbon dioxide in sunlight and excrete oxygen.

With higher living things respiration becomes increasingly complicated. The process can now be divided into two phases: external and internal respiration. The external phase is concerned with the intake of air into the respiratory organs and the transfer of the oxygen to the blood, which carries it to the cells which use it. The internal phase is the process that takes place inside the cell. The blood provides the cell with oxygen and takes from it the waste products of combustion, carbon dioxide or a solution of it in water called carbonic acid.

The organs of external respiration in the animal kingdom are very varied, but all the different forms are based on three main types: the tree-like, branched system of air-tubes or tracheæ in insects, the gills of fishes, and the nose, windpipe and lungs of the higher animals, including man. The skin can also play a part in respiration, but only does so in small, thin-skinned animals, such as the amphibia, where it can act as an extra organ of breathing. In most other animals the skin does not breathe in the sense of taking up oxygen and giving off carbon dioxide, but only serves for the evaporation of water.

Respiration in man is controlled by a nervous centre in the spinal cord of the neck. This "respiratory centre" is sensitive to the slightest variations of carbon dioxide concentration in the blood. It immediately sends orders to the muscles of the chest and diaphragm to increase or decrease the breathing movements according to the requirements of the body. It ensures that we do not stop breathing when we are asleep and it is the only nervous centre of the body which has a voluntary as well as an involuntary control. It is also very easily damaged. If a man breaks his neck he does not die because of damage to the spine, but because a fragment of a vertebra enters and destroys the respiratory centre.

Air should enter the body through the nose, which has the task of preparing it for the lungs. The nose warms the air and frees it from dust and germs. The turbinal bones, which are richly supplied with blood, act like the radiators of a central heating system, and together with the tear-glands and tonsils they provide the air with the required moisture.

Hairs inside the spaces of the nose keep out foreign bodies and prevent them from entering the wind-pipe or the lungs. Lower down in our respiratory system these hairs are replaced by a fine lawn of hair-like structures, the ciliated epithelium. The fine cilia on this epithelium work in co-operation (they would look like a waving field of corn if they were enlarged), and their ingenious, whip-like motion sweeps even the finest dust particles outside the respiratory tracts after a few hours, rather like a chain of men transporting coal or rubble. To get an idea of the extent of the work done by the ciliated epithelium, we have only to realise that it moves an estimated thirty-five to fifty-five pounds of dust during a sixty-year life span of a city dweller. This total includes only the finest particles because the coarser pieces which are inhaled through the throat and into the wind-pipe are ejected by coughing. During a cough wind speeds of over 300 feet per second are reached inside the larynx, a far greater air velocity even than that of a hurricane.

The upper portion of the nose contains the olfactory nerves, the main function of which is to act as a danger signal. They test the air for smells, and tell the brain whether we are in a good or bad atmosphere. Our breathing is regulated, with-

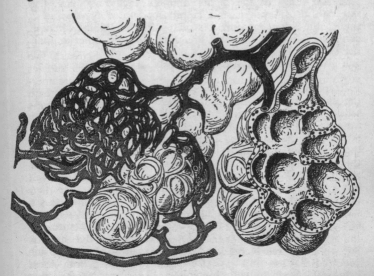

Each alveolus is surrounded by a network of the finest bloodvessels.

out our knowledge, by the influence of the olfactory nerves and becomes stronger in good air and weaker in bad.

After the air has gone through the nose it enters the semi-rigid wind-pipe, which is about as wide as a thumb. From here it divides and travels through the bronchi and their branches to the lobes of the lungs. These are the vital centres of the breathing apparatus, which supply the body with the essential oxygen. One can compare them to a very efficient pair of bellows. The lungs, together with the heart and the large blood vessels occupy the whole space of the chest. Their lower ends rest on the diaphragm, which divides the thorax from the abdomen. Their inner sides surround the heart. Deep furrows divide the right lung into three and the left lung into two lobes. The lungs and inner walls of the chest cavity are lined with a sheet of epithelium, the pleura, called the parietal and visceral pleura respectively.

Like a tree dividing into branches and twigs of decreasing size, the bronchi branch out into increasingly small tubes until a mass of nearly 230,000 tiny bronchioles fills the whole space in the lungs. Each of the bronchioles ends in a minute cluster of bubbles, like bunches of grapes, each one smaller than a pin-head. These are the alveoli, and their exact number is not known, but estimates range from 300 to 1800 million. This is not all, however. The tiny alveoli are surrounded by the even smaller and finer capillaries. The capillary is the smallest blood vessel inside the human body, and those in our muscles alone, if placed end to end, would reach two and a half times round the world. These hardly visible tubules surround the alveoli like a dense net, and only a gossamer-thin membrane divides the two structures. With every breath we take there is an exchange of gases across this membrane between the blood and the lungs.

How can we visualise this exchange?

Let us go back to the subject of external respiration for a moment. When we inhale we do not expand the lungs themselves but enlarge the cage of the ribs. At the same time the diaphragm contracts and changes from its original upward curvature to the shape of a flat plate. The lungs follow their enlarged envelope like the bellows of an accordion, and a negative pressure develops inside the expanded alveoli. Air streams through the wind-pipe and the bronchi until it reaches the alveoli and the immediate neighbourhood of the capillaries, where the red blood corpuscles are waiting to take up the required oxygen and give off carbon dioxide. Both these processes simply follow the law of gas pressure, which is that an equilibrium is reached when two substances of different concentration meet each other. The blood inside the capillaries flows around the alveoli for only one short second, but during that second the miracle of respiration, the exchange of gases, takes place. It is due to this process that the cells of our body always have sufficient oxygen. The red blood corpuscles take up the oxygen and release it again when they come into contact with the cells, taking back carbon dioxide on their return to the lungs. This exchange is repeated continuously as long as the heart beats and circulates the blood.

The rhythmic expansion and contraction of the lungs and the tireless pumping of the heart is not enough to insure

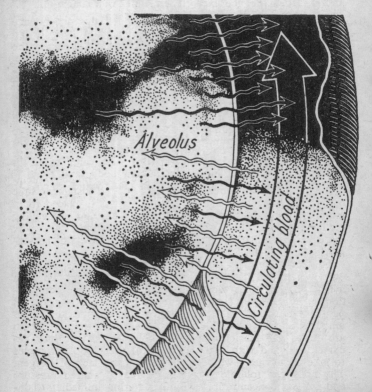

A cross-section through an alveolus. Oxygen seeps through the thin membrane and is carried by the blood to the cells of the body (black arrows). The blood transfers carbon dioxide to the alveolus in the opposite direction (white arrows).

an adequate supply of oxygen to the body. There is a third essential factor: the air we breathe must be at a certain pressure. For our respiration to function properly this pressure must be neither too great nor too small.

I have already, in chapter two, mentioned the enormous weight (equivalent to pressure) which the atmosphere exerts on the earth and on men. Just as deep-sea creatures are adapted to the pressure of the water, we are adapted to the pressure of the air. If the tension in our body cells and the blood pressure in our veins were not great enough to counteract this pressure, the weight of the atmosphere would squash us as flat as a postage stamp.

Many of us have personally experienced this dependence on pressure. If one ascends in a funicular railway or an aeroplane, one feels a cracking and buzzing in the ears as the body tries to adapt itself to the decreasing air pressure. These pressure sensations on the ear-drum are purely mechanical signs of a disturbance of the pressure equilibrium between the air outside and inside the ear. While the pressure outside falls during the ascent, that in the middle ear remains the same as it was on the ground. In consequence the ear-drum bulges outwards. During a descent the opposite occurs and the ear-drum bulges noticeably inwards. It takes some time before the pressure on both sides is again in equilibrium. Frequent swallowing accelerates the equalising of the pressure. Each time you swallow, the mucous membrane, which usually covers the opening of the eustachian tube connecting the mouth and the middle ear, is displaced for a moment, thus allowing an exchange of air and a levelling out of pressure. Once you realise this you understand why the stewardess distributes chewing-gum and sweets to passengers before a flight.

The higher we rise the harder it becomes for us to adapt ourselves to the decreasing air pressure. Although up to a height of nine miles the air has roughly the same composition as at sea-level (approximately 21 per cent oxygen, 78 per cent nitrogen, 0.03 per cent carbon dioxide and small amounts of rare gases), it grows increasingly thinner. There are fewer gas particles per unit volume, the pressure becomes less, and with it the capacity of the blood corpuscles to take up oxygen—we begin to suffer from lack of oxygen. The body can tolerate a certain degree of altered pressure and oxygen concentration without suffering immediate damage. Let us imagine that we were surrounded by pure oxygen. Naturally our respiration would not get worse, but, contrary to expectation, it would not improve either. The reason for this is easily explained. The red blood corpuscles which are the oxygen carriers inside our bodies cannot absorb unlimited amounts; like the buckets of a water-wheel they can take up only a certain quantity. The reservoir from which they obtain their oxygen, the normal atmosphere, is usually more than enough to fill them to capacity. Experiments have shown that the normal oxygen content of air of 21 per cent can sink as low as 8 per cent without impairing respiration. This is a safety margin which Nature has provided for our oxygen supply, and only if the content falls below 8 per cent is there any danger.

A mountaineer notices the decrease of air pressure at about ten thousand feet. Above this height, and up to about twenty-three thousand feet, the body can to a certain degree acclimatise itself to the thinner air. Three factors play the main role in this adaptation. Firstly, the heart beats faster and increases the amount of blood passing through the lungs. This means that more red blood corpuscles take up and carry oxygen per unit of time. Secondly, the respiratory centre accelerates the rate of breathing to compensate for the disadvantages of the thin atmosphere by increasing the amount of air inhaled. (To demonstrate these two reactions you do not have to climb high mountains—any strong physical exertion, even on level ground, will produce them.) Thirdly, there is an increased production of red corpuscles by the bone marrow, induced by a lack of oxygen. This is also for the purpose of transporting more oxygen per unit of time. Since red blood corpuscles cannot be made instantaneously, mountaineers who wish to reach a height of more than twenty-three thousand feet must remain at intermediate camps for several days or weeks. They must give the body a chance to form new corpuscles and acclimatise it gradually to the altering conditions.

Despite the adaptability of our bodies, climbs of over sixteen thousand feet remain adventures which only well trained, healthy and strong-willed people can undertake. Above this height even trained climbers can only proceed with great difficulty, because the body tends to conserve oxygen and wants to cut down on all activity. Members of expeditions report that at eighteen thousand feet they already had the feeling of performing the hardest physical labour while suffering from double pneumonia. The Swiss mountaineer Dittert took two and a half hours to put on his boots at a height of twenty-three thousand feet on Mount Everest. His colleague Lambert took five hours to advance two hundred yards—which means that each step took more than thirty seconds.

Bodily fatigue is one of the things men suffer at great

heights; the other is a sort of drunkenness or intoxication which makes them minimise or even disregard the dangers around them. Lambert describes this feeling: "We walked as if through cotton-wool. We grasped for a hold that wasn't there, and laughed when we gripped emptiness." According to the experience of the English Himalayan expert Shipton, a mountaineer near the top of Mount Everest is like "a sick man climbing in a dream." Dr. Herrligkoffer of Munich, who led the Nanga Parbat expedition of 1953, writes that at great heights the joys of climbing are blotted out. Apart from this an exaggerated touchiness appears, which creates a problem among the colleagues of an expedition. This leads to friction in some cases, contentiousness and finally to mountain madness among those with a psychopathic tendency.

In the thin air of heights above twenty-three thousand feet nearly all the reactions of the human body become unpredictable, changeable and dangerous. Our adaptability soon reaches its limits. Faces take on a blue-red colour due to the increased red blood corpuscles in the arteries and veins. Migraine saps the determination. Loss of sleep and appetite alternate with a raging hunger for sweets, and a nagging thirst quickly raises the water requirements.

Above twenty-six thousand feet the "region of death" begins. The lack of oxygen produces a feeling of limpness and apathy. The climber can only survive by taking oxygen or drugs such as Pervitin which stimulate the respiratory centre.

An increase in air pressure likewise presents problems connected with breathing. A diver, for instance, can hardly expand his chest because of the water pressure on it, and has to breathe air at greater than atmospheric pressure to be able to obtain sufficient oxygen. His body is exposed not only to the pressure of the air, but to the column of water under which he is working. At 33 feet (5½ fathoms), for example, he requires air at an extra pressure of two atmospheres, at 66 feet (11 fathoms) three, and at 163 feet (25½ fathoms) six atmospheres. The modern Cousteau-Gagnan compressed-air breathing apparatus for skin-divers is provided with an automatic valve which delivers air at the correct pressure for the depth of dive. This valve resembles a gas tap which changes from closed to fully open on diving and in the reverse direction when returning to the surface.

Further dangers connected with breathing await the diver. The greater the water pressure on his body, the more nitrogen will dissolve in his blood, for the solubility of a gas in a liquid depends on pressure. If a diver returns to the surface too quickly, he does not give his blood a chance to get rid of the dissolved gas released by the decrease in pressure.

At such times his blood resembles the soda-water in a syphon, the valve of which has suddenly been released. As in the soda-water, nitrogen bubbles form in the blood and, with the release in pressure, try to escape. But since these bubbles cannot burst anywhere, they wander about and finally block small arteries. This causes the notorious "bends," air embolism and heart attacks, which can prove fatal. Divers returning from the bottom must, therefore, scrupulously observe the prescribed times of ascent so that their blood can be gradually depressurised, thus avoiding the formation of these bubbles.

Another danger for divers is a type of narcosis. This attacks men below a depth of about 130 feet (22 fathoms). As with a climber at great heights, the body no longer reacts normally; surrounding dangers seem unimportant; objects appear to dance before the eyes, and a dull euphoria clouds the senses. This "depth intoxication" is probably due to an overdose of nitrogen, and if the diver does not stop his descent at once and rise to lesser depths he may, in his ecstasy, spit out the mouthpiece of his breathing apparatus and drown. This happened to the French skin-diver Maurice Fargues. In 1947 he reached a depth of 396 feet (66 fathoms) in the Mediterranean wearing a compressed-air breathing apparatus. He scratched his name on a marking plate on the plumb-line before he became a victim of this intoxication. When he was pulled from the water he was already dead, and the mouthpiece of his breathing tube dangled on his chest.

Both these phenomena, mountain madness and depth intoxication, are abnormal reactions of the body to changed atmospheric conditions. We need not fear these conditions as long as we stay on the ground, for there the surrounding air has the same concentration that it already had millions of years ago. Our bodies have become accustomed to this concentration during the process of evolution, and we can alter the supply of air, without altering its concentration, by merely regulating the rate of our respiration according to the requirements of our bodies.

The slightest physical exertion leads to deep and satisfying breathing. A man at rest normally exchanges about one-seventh of all the air in his lungs (just under one pint) with each breath. Doctors multiply this value by the number of breaths per minute (about fifteen) and call the result the "basic respiration rate." It amounts to 1.65 gallons for a man at rest. During a gentle walk it is doubled. During strenuous climbing it is multiplied by ten and during rowing competitions it can increase up to twenty times. During such moments of extreme physical exertion our lungs fill about forty times each minute and inhale up to thirty-three gallons of air, enough to inflate fifteen toy balloons.

Normally we breathe by moving the ribs and the diaphragm, but these movements can be separated. If we only move the ribs we indulge in pure chest breathing, and if the diaphragm alone is working (i.e. when lying on our backs) we are stomach breathing. Both types combined give a full, healthy respiration which should be practised whenever possible. Correct breathing was a matter of great importance to the ancient Greeks. To them an education lacking respiratory training was unthinkable. They systematically practised correct aeration of the lungs for speaking, playing, dancing, and singing, laying a special stress on the power of the diaphragm. If we study the statues of young men of this era, the Apollo of Phidias for instance, we are struck by the strongly developed stomach muscles in the groin, which give the male body perfect proportions. Later races have neglected this respiratory training and the modern "office man" (if the reader will forgive an ugly phrase) often breathes in a frighteningly inadequate manner. In consequence the body not only loses its external tension but obtains too little oxygen. This can cause all sorts of damage.

19

MAN OUTWITS THE AIR

EVER SINCE man raised his eyes to the sky and saw the flight of the birds it has been his desire to emulate them; he longed to rise high above the earth and sail away. The Greek myths already tell of flying men: Dædalus and his son Icarus made themselves wings of feathers and wax to escape the power of King Minos of Crete. Dædalus managed to fly to Sicily but his son Icarus came too close to the sun, which melted the wax in his wings, and he crashed into the sea before his father's eyes.

Leonardo da Vinci was the first man of our era to consider seriously flight by muscle-power. Around 1500 he sketched the first designs for a flying machine. But he was unable to fulfil his dream, nor has any other man as yet been able to imitate the birds and move through the air by his own power. Modern flying technique has really cheated mankind out of the age-old desire to fly, for in reality men do not fly their aeroplanes but are flown by them.

The German technician Otto Lilienthal made history by being the first human being to glide through the air in a man-made machine, in 1891. His apparatus was a primitive biplane. The pilot sat, or rather dangled, at the centre of gravity, for his legs protruded through the bottom and served to steer the machine. By throwing his legs forwards, backwards or sideways he changed the course of his artificial bird upwards or downwards or to the left or right. Lilienthal is said to have made more than a thousand successful glides during which he remained in the air up to twenty seconds and covered distances up to eight hundred feet. For those times that was an impressive piece of bravura. Unfortunately the ingenious engineer soon became a victim of his own daring. On the 9th of August, 1896, near Rhinow (close to Berlin) a sudden squall proved too strong to counteract with his legs. The machine capsized and the pilot was killed.

Lilienthal's experiments were the first to provide practical knowledge about heavier-than-air machines, but machines lighter than air were already known in China around 1300. The Chinese, realising that hot air is lighter than cold, made hot air balloons. These balloons actually rose, although not very far, but nobody dared to rise with them. This feat was first achieved by the Montgolfier brothers of France. They constructed a balloon with a capacity of 100,000 cubic feet, made of cloth and covered with paper on the inside. They called it the "Montgolfière." The first flight took place near Paris on the 21st of November, 1783. The spherical monster was anchored with ropes and a fire lit beneath it, filling it with hot air from below. Large crowds watched the richly decorated balloon rise slowly upwards, carrying with it the courageous pilots J. F. Pilâtre de Rozier and the Marquis d'Arlandes.

Hot air balloons were superseded by gas filled ones, which could reach heights of many thousand feet. The American test-pilot J. W. Kittinger reached 29,261 metres (about 18 miles) above Minnesota in the gondola of his helium-filled balloon on the 2nd of June, 1957. He remained at this height for two hours and made many measurements before releasing some of the helium and returning to earth. On the 20th of August, 1957, David Simons, a doctor in the United States Air Force, exceeded Kittinger's achievement by rising to a height of nineteen miles in a similar balloon. From this altitude he could have seen Edinburgh, Brest and Cologne if he had started over London. Simons stayed in the air for thirty-two hours, twenty-seven of them at a height above seventeen miles. The view from his seat in the "celestial gallery" had never before been seen by man. The most astounding thing was the interplay of atmospheric colours. He reported by radio that: "All colours seem to have been bleached from the heavens. The sky is dark, a purple-black which is indescribable." Later he said: "No sunset on earth was ever as beautiful as this. . . ."

Simons's gondola was barely as big as a telephone booth. It was loaded with five hundredweight of scientific apparatus, amongst which the pilot crouched on a folding seat. Despite this lack of space, the gondola offered some degree of safety. If the helium-filled balloon were to have burst, Simons could have escaped quickly from the air-tight chamber and would have had some chance to parachute back to earth alive.

The successor to the gas-filled balloon was the airship. The first models were more or less at the mercy of air currents, but after the invention of the petrol engine they were provided with propellers and rudders. The era of the dirigibles had begun and many new records were set up. The German hydrogen-filled dirigible, *Graf Zeppelin*, for instance, crossed the Atlantic 130 times. The development of flight, however, could not advance along the lines of these cumbersome "flying cigars." They floated across the skies like ponderous modern saurians; very impressive, but not suited to our age of rapid movement. Apart from this it was very expensive to provide helium, which was preferred to the easily inflammable hydrogen. After the catastrophic fire on the *Hindenburg* at Lakehurst in May 1937 no important new dirigibles were built. Their day was over.

The future of flying clearly lay with machines that were heavier than air. The layman can never really understand how the awkward metal structure of the aeroplane can remain aloft. The secret of this mystery lies mainly in the clever construction of the wings. They are gently curved, and as the air passes the curved surface a negative pressure is developed on the convex side and a positive pressure on the concave one. Both these forces act in unison to lift the wing upwards and keep the aeroplane airborne.

Otto Lilienthal already had the beginnings of this idea in his mind when he undertook his risky flights in the last years of the nineteenth century. It was fully worked out for the first time by two bicycle mechanics from Ohio ten years later. They also proved that rudders and elevators can steer an aeroplane more effectively than the dangling legs of the pilot. These pioneers were the brothers Wright, who made the first powered flights of twelve to fifty-nine seconds with

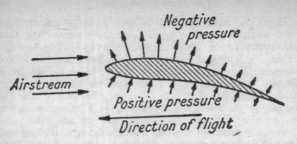

Two forces acting together in the same direction on the
wings of an aeroplane.

a sixteen horsepower engine on the 17th of December, 1903,
at the Kitty Hawk peninsula near Norfolk, Virginia.

Now things began to move rapidly. In 1909 Bleriot flew
across the English Channel. In 1915 Junkers built the first
all-metal aeroplane. Byrd crossed the North Pole in 1926
and Lindbergh flew from New York to Paris in 33½ hours in
1927. Towards the end of the Second World War the first jet-
fighters streaked across the sky and in 1947 the American experimental machine Bell XS-1 exceeded the speed of sound
for the first time. In 1952 the jet and rocket powered "Sky-
rocket" unofficially reached a height of fifteen miles and a
speed of 1400 miles per hour. The first passenger flight from
Copenhagen to Los Angeles via the North Pole took place in
1954. The British experimental Fairey Delta FD2 set the
official world record at 1032 miles per hour in 1956, but this
was soon exceeded unofficially by the rocket-plane Bell X-2
with about 1860 m.p.h. Modern unpiloted rockets reached
several times the speed of sound after only two seconds and
experimental multi-stage rockets achieved nearly ten times
the speed of sound with 6560 m.p.h.

New inventions and records pursue one another. Machines
with an increasingly higher ceiling of flight roll from the
workshops. Heavy long-range jet-bombers can already attain
supersonic speeds. Plans for jet-fighters which cannot only
fly but can pursue an enemy into the sea are even now on the
drawing-board. New alloys and new designs are being produced at full throttle with the object of surmounting the
"heat-barrier"—the phenomenon which causes aeroplanes
at high supersonic speeds to glow by aerial friction. It will
not be long before the first man roars out of the atmosphere
of our planet and starts his journey into space.

Let us remain on the ground for a little. There is an important problem behind all the work on the drawing-boards,

in the laboratories and on the airfields. Can man fly even higher and faster without running into danger? Is there a limit beyond which death inevitably awaits him?

There is no getting around the fact that a pilot has to face and surmount medical problems once he takes to the air. In the chapter on respiration we have already dealt with the dangers of great heights. Some of the difficulties that face a mountaineer are also valid for the pilot. The higher he rises the thinner the air becomes. At just over three and a half miles the air pressure is already only half that at sea-level and it becomes difficult to supply the body with oxygen. Breathing becomes laboured and further ascent can lead to fainting. At ten and a half miles an unprotected pilot becomes unconscious after about fifteen seconds, and a few minutes later a lack of oxygen in the brain causes damage and perhaps death. To ensure a normal oxygen supply at great heights a pilot needs an apparatus which provides this essential gas at the required pressure.

The decreasing air pressure would affect the pilot in three ways: firstly his blood (if he were still alive) would begin to boil at about thirteen and a half miles (see also page 26); secondly, a too rapid ascent can cause bubbles of gas in the blood vessels, similar to those of a diver rising rapidly to the surface (see also page 143); thirdly, the hollow spaces of the body can suffer pain and damage unless the pilot is completely healthy. Hollow spaces such as the lungs, intestines, frontal sinuses and inner ears are filled with air which would normally expand to reach an equilibrium with the decreased air pressure outside the body. Since these spaces cannot expand, or only to a limited extent, equilibrium can only be attained by expelling some of the air which fills them. A healthy body reacts in this way, but if the pilot suffers from a cold or some other disturbance in these parts of the body, a rapid ascent can lead to painful and damaging consequences.

The pressurised cabin is a well-proven method of counteracting such undesirable effects. It forms a hermetic protection and surrounds the pilot with a small, familiar world of pressure condition at sea-level even at a great height. The pressurised cabin coupled with air-conditioning is already used in many passenger planes. Air is usually supplied by a pump which sucks in air from the outside, compresses it and pushes it inside the cabin. Automatic valves then keep the pressure constant. This method can only be used up to a height of about fifteen miles. We know that the ozone layer lies between fifteen and thirty miles, and this layer, which protects us by capturing a large amount of the dangerous

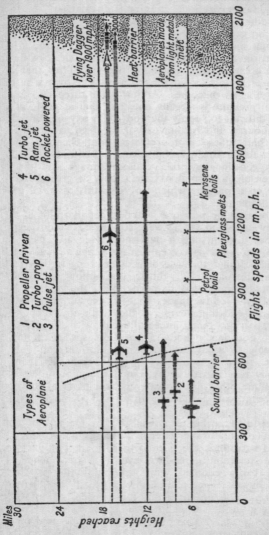

This diagram gives the figures. On the left (vertically) are the heights they can reach, and at the bottom (horizontally) are the speeds of which they are capable. The shaded line in front of each type of aeroplane gives the respective possibilities of their further development.

short-wave sun rays, would play havoc if it went inside the cabin. The ozone would destroy rubber, corrode metal parts and poison the passengers.

The value of cabins supplied by compressors above fifteen miles is, therefore, doubtful. At such heights an aeroplane needs a cabin which is supplied by compressed air from the inside. The gases, preferably a mixture of oxygen and helium, are carried in cylinders and the exhaled gases are "detoxicated."

Another danger is that damage to the cabin may lead to an escape of the pressurised air. Such an accident befell the Amerian tourist Jack Rodney Nash during the Easter of 1957 above Iraq. Nash had unsuspectingly fallen asleep leaning against the porthole of a French passenger plane when the glass was shattered by unknown forces (perhaps a meteorite; perhaps his diamond ring scratching the pane?). The air escaping through the porthole sucked Nash clean out of the plane and he fell to his death 20,000 feet below.

Experts have long racked their brains trying to devise a way of surrounding the body of the pilot with air at the required pressure, and have finally invented a suit which serves as a miniature pressurised cabin. It consists of a skin-tight, impermeable covering which inflates automatically if the pressure suddenly falls, and this compensates for the lost air pressure without which the pilot could not breathe or live.

Acceleration and its effect on the human body has also become a major problem of flying. The modern pilot is exposed increasingly to this force. Acceleration is not directly related to speed but, according to physicists, is an expression of change of speed in terms of time. We will later give examples of how acceleration can increase or decrease the weight of the body or in special cases even lead to its complete suspension.

Acceleration is measured in units of "G" which are related to the gravitational pull of the earth (one G). This pull is demonstrated by the tendency of all objects to fall downwards, and its magnitude is expressed by the weight of the object.

Objects at rest always retain their normal weight, but if the speed at which an object moves changes, or if it alters its direction (so that centrifugal forces come into play), its weight also changes. Taking a sharp bend in a fast moving car we are forced against the door with a weight greater than that registered on our bathroom scales.

The forces of acceleration in a car are nothing compared to those developed in a modern aeroplane. A jet or rocket-fighter can produce forces of up to 6 G, or even more, which means that a pilot normally weighing about one hundred and eighty pounds can increase to over half a ton during take-off, landing or when flying in a curve. A good example is the catapult take-off from aircraft carriers at sea. Nowadays this is no longer done by hydraulic methods but with steam pressure. The aeroplane attains speeds of several hundred miles per hour during a sixty-foot run. Only a thoroughly healthy, well-trained and correctly strapped pilot can withstand such accelerations. A high pressure forces him against the back of his seat, and the opposite effect occurs when the landing aeroplane is stopped by ropes; the pilot is pressed forward against his safety-belt.

The force of G can manifest itself in two ways during a curved flight at high speeds. During a horizontal curve, an upward loop or when pulling out of a dive it acts from the head towards the feet of the pilot, and the blood flows into the lower parts of his body. The head, neck and chest become less rich in blood, the internal organs grow as heavy as lead and sink downwards, while an enormous force pushes the pilot down on his seat. Experiments have shown that pilots suffer a visual black-out after only ten seconds at forces of 4 to 5 G. The blood supply to the brain is no longer sufficient to enable the optic nerves to function.

The second type of action of G is from the feet towards the head, when the blood flows from the lower regions upward (as when doing an outside loop). This is usually even more dangerous. The pilot suffers from a "red-out," his head becomes hot and heavy, and if a force of 3 G acts for more than fifteen seconds, sensitive blood vessels in the brain and eyes can burst, leading to cerebral hæmorrhage and permanently impaired sight.

Ingenious devices have been invented to prevent this upward or downward rush of blood. The modern flying-suit has a pair of air tubes across the calves, a pair across the thighs and one across the chest. These tubes are automatically inflated according to requirements and press on the arteries and veins, preventing the displacement of too much blood. They only counteract up to two, or at the most two and a half G, and are powerless against greater forces.

What is the greatest acceleration that the human body can withstand? What happens when the pilot has to leave his aeroplane, perhaps at supersonic speeds? At the beginning of the Second World War the German air force carried out a series of test flights and dives to solve this vital question. I have been told that test pilots dived a Ju. 88 machine eleven times in sixty-eight minutes, withstanding forces up to 6.3 G. After the war the United States Air Force doctor, John Paul Stapp, carried out a series of remarkable experiments with the same object in view. His experimental machine was a rocket-driven steel sledge, twelve feet long, running on a dead-straight set of 2700 feet long rails at Alamogordo in New Mexico. Nine rockets brought the sledge to a speed of about 620 m.p.h. inside a few seconds. It raced along the rails for about six seconds. During this time slow-motion cameras, blood-pressure and pulse meters recorded the effect on the passenger. Stapp was strapped into his special seat during the trials and held a rubber ball in his mouth to prevent a dislocation of the jaw. His head was protected by a crash-helmet which was fastened to the back of the seat. The sledge started off like a bullet. The braking mechanism was Stapp's personal invention. A shovel-like paddle was lowered into a water-filled trough between the rails. This brake stopped the sledge inside 1.5 seconds, and the forward motion of the passenger pressed him against the safety-belt, blew out his cheeks and pushed his eyeballs forward. The force developed during the braking equalled that of a car hitting a brick wall at a hundred miles an hour. "I saw bright yellow and red-coloured spots," Stapp declared after a trial run in 1954. "The pain in the eyes was so acute that I hardly noticed the shock of braking. It took eight minutes before I could see clearly again."

Stapp's travels to the edge of supersonic speeds have increased our knowledge of the physiology of flight. He proved that the human body can stand up to accelerations of 6 G, something that even experts believed to be impossible. Stapp also showed that a pilot can withstand the obscure forces of G better when in a reclining position than when sitting. The reclining seats in some modern aeroplanes cannot prevent the gallon or so of blood in the body of the pilot from weighing four gallons when submitted to a force of 4 G. Since the heart does not have a similar fourfold increase in strength, it must perform a task which strains it in the long run, and which may lead to permanent injury.

The problem of abandoning a damaged aeroplane is just as important as that of acceleration. Since an unprotected pilot leaving a supersonic machine in the usual manner would be killed at once by the murderous air stream or at least lose some limbs, methods of preventing this had to be contrived. The cabin of some fast aeroplanes is constructed in such a way that it can be separated from the rest of the machine in case of accidents by pressing a lever, after which it floats to earth on a parachute. This solution presents mechanical difficulties and is only feasible at great heights, since otherwise the cabin would strike the earth before the parachute had time to open.

A better method is the light ejector-seat which is shot out of the aeroplane either upward or downward. A plexiglass helmet and other safety devices protect the pilot against the air current. In Lockheed aeroplanes, for instance, the pilot in the ejector-seat pulls a D-shaped handle in cases of danger. This releases a series of automatic reactions which are designed to bring the pilot back to earth alive. During the first second the pilot is fastened to his seat by steel springs to prevent his arms and legs being damaged in the following manœuvres. Next the seat is shot downwards out of the aeroplane. A steel plate then unfolds from the bottom of the seat, as soon as the pilotless machine is at a safe distance, protecting the pilot like the windshield of a car. Fin-like projections and rudimentary wings unfold and prevent him turning over and over. Everything is done to keep him on a stable course until the parachute opens automatically at a height of three miles. The mechanism of the parachute is coupled to an altimeter which opens it sooner if the pilot has to jump at lower altitudes. The Lockheed ejector-seat is said to be safe at a height of only 450 feet. The questions of how the human body would react to the forces of ejection and the shock of the opening parachute have not yet been completely solved.

The human body has to adapt itself to high G values, or it can be partially protected by mechanical means, but new problems appear when the force of G becomes equal to nought, that is when the body becomes weightless. This peculiar phenomenon occurs when the gravitational pull of the earth is cancelled out by an equal and opposite force. The odd sensations experienced in such a case are familiar to anyone who has taken a ride on the scenic railway at a fair-ground. After the train has gone through a "valley" and is rolling over a "mountain" the passengers are lifted from their seats for a fraction of a second, during which they feel as if they had no weight. They have a sinking sensation. The upward force imparted by the train is equal to the gravitational pull towards the earth; both are in equilibrium and G equals nought.

Experienced pilots can prolong such moments of weightlessness up to forty-five seconds. They fly at high speeds along a track that is parabolically inclined towards the earth. Loose objects in the aeroplane rise into the air and remain suspended there. Liquids poured from vessels form drops which hang about the cabin. Passengers lose all sensation of weight. This short-lived feeling gives a foretaste of conditions awaiting us in space when interplanetary travel has become a reality.

How does a man react when the gravitational pull is suddenly removed? The problem of long-term weightlessness, due to space travel, is still unanswerable. The short-term experiments do not seem to reveal serious disadvantages. One of the sixteen participants in a flight during the International Astronautical Congress of September 1956 in Rome declared that he would prefer the weightless condition to all other methods of relaxation. Most of the other passengers experienced a pleasant sensation. Some felt a pressure in their eye-sockets, others perspired or suffered a mild headache. According to the American doctor Gerathewohl there is a sensation as of the body swimming during the weightless period. When the eyes are closed all feeling of orientation is lost, but there is a feeling of extreme refreshment.

Modern aeronautics have to deal with another special case, movement through the air at speeds previously attained only by missiles. If an aeroplane moves through the lower layers of the atmosphere at about 715 miles per hour it reaches the speed of sound. Scientists call this "Mach 1" after the Austrian physicist Ernst Mach. At Mach 1 strange things begin to happen. The molecules of the air, which had time to avoid the aeroplane without jostling each other because they were warned by the preceding pressure wave, are now completely unprepared. At sonic and supersonic speeds the aeroplane approaches too suddenly. It hits the molecules without warning, pushes them together and forces its way through their compressed mass. The aeroplane is in the position of a motor-cyclist who at high speed suddenly meets a dense crowd of people on an open road. If the noise of the machine has given insufficient time for the people to disperse they are mown down. The supersonic aeroplane strikes the molecules of the air in just this way and compresses them so that the carefully streamlined design of the wings and body is no longer effective. Finally the molecules part, as in an explosion, when the aeroplane breaks the sound barrier, giving rise to the notorious shock wave which may burst windowpanes and even ear-drums.

A supersonic machine is exposed to far more violent forces than a subsonic one. Pressure waves rattle, tear and push the body and wings mercilessly. Only the most resistant materials and the well-planned construction of the various parts can withstand such buffets.

Aeroplanes which fly at twice the speed of sound or more encounter a new danger. The friction with the air molecules generates so much heat that the metal begins to glow or even melt. Petrol starts to boil in an aeroplane flying at Mach 1.4 (1000 m.p.h. and 7 miles height); plexiglass melts at

Mach 1.7 (1200 m.p.h.); kerosene fuel boils at Mach 2 (1430 m.p.h.); and glass softens at Mach 3.6 (2550 m.p.h.). The only possible way to combat this heat-barrier is to instal a cooling mechanism and to use suitable metals, such as titanium, niobium, molybdenum and rhenium, which are already being tested in the laboratory.

Where will the development of modern aeronautics lead us? There is no doubt that the next step is a journey into outer space. To-day the question is no longer whether this is possible but merely when it will take place. When will the first human being clear the atmosphere, develop space stations on artificial moons and set foot on another planet?

When the Russian technicians sent the first artificial moon, "sputnik," into an orbit about five hundred miles above the earth, on the 4th of October, 1957, man had proved that he can leave this planet. In the meantime other man-made satellites have been launched into space and circle the earth at great speed. They obey the laws of the heavens, the same laws in accordance with which the planets circle the sun. The centrifugal force which pulls the satellite outwards in its orbit is exactly balanced by the attractive force of the earth. It is due to this carefully calculated equilibrium that such small moons can circle our planet for a long time without either falling back to earth or escaping into space.

If an artificial moon is sent so high that it escapes completely from the atmosphere, it can theoretically travel around the earth indefinitely, for there is no resistance to its movement. On the other hand it is exposed to forces in outer space about which we know comparatively little. What is the effect of solar radiation? Does its pressure influence the orbit of the satellite? What about cosmic dust and meteorites? Our artificial satellites should help us to answer these and many other questions.

If a satellite does not go quite so high, it is doomed —sooner or later—because of the braking power of the atmosphere. The original orbit, which may have been circular, gradually becomes a spiral as the satellite comes closer and closer to the earth. Finally it crashes like a meteor and either hits the crust of the earth, or burns away like a shooting star due to the enormous frictional heat when it meets the lower layers of the atmosphere.

In general the artificial moons serve two main experimental purposes. They should help to elucidate some unsolved riddles about our planet and its atmosphere, and they should also prepare mankind for journeys into space. It may well be that most of the people alive to-day will be able to say of that event: "I can remember when . . . !"

20

MAN-MADE STARLIGHT

HAVE YOU EVER WONDERED why the sky between the stars is never completely black, even on a moonless night? Why there is a faint glow, barely visible but too strong to pass unnoticed? All the stars taken together are not bright enough to account for this strange light, and yet it is there. Where does it come from?

The scientists of many nations have worked on the secret of this phenomenon. To-day we know the answer. It was found in the course of an ascent by an experimental American Aerobee rocket, itself a milestone in our knowledge of space-travel. This rocket helped to light the first man-made starlight.

That is the end of the story. Let us return to the beginning.

Where there is light there is not only shadow but also something burning, or at least some change of energy. This basic principle of physics also applies to the faint nocturnal light. Since the time of Bunsen (the middle of the nineteenth century) the most reliable method of finding out what causes the glow in the skies has been spectrum analysis. This consists of breaking the light into its component parts by a glass prism, in the same manner in which tiny water droplets in the atmosphere break up the sunlight to form a rainbow. From the composition of the colours and the width of their bands the expert can accurately deduce the type of substance which causes the light he is investigating. He is able to do this because every compound gives off its own type of light when it burns and has its own specific spectrum.

It was not difficult to break the nocturnal light into its component parts by means of delicate optical instruments and to discover the substances that caused it. The answer was that glow was created by oxygen and nitrogen at a height of more than thirty-seven miles.

This only solved the first part of the riddle, and left the second unexplained. How did these gases cause the light? The most important work on this problem was carried out by a group of American scientists under the leadership of Dr. Murray Zelikoff. He carefully studied the results obtained from rockets which had been sent to great heights for experimental purposes. These rockets carried instruments which gave information about air pressure, temperature, radiations and other properties of the air at great heights. Zelikoff was particularly interested in the results obtained above the ozone layer. This layer lies about twenty miles above the earth and its average depth is about twenty-five miles. It contains many molecules of ozone (each consisting of three atoms of oxygen) and acts as a shield against the dangerous and powerful ultra-violet rays that bombard us.

He could only guess what took place above the ozone layer, but thanks to the rockets we now know that there is a whole witches' cauldron of chemical reactions, caused by the play of sunlight on air particles. Up there the sun's rays have not yet met the "ozone filter" and the full intensity of the ultra-violet rays is at work.

This discovery carried Zelikoff forward a great deal. Then he had another idea. What would happen if he created an artificial sky in the laboratory, reconstructing the conditions in the upper atmosphere, and then irradiated it with ultra-violet rays from a synthetic sun?

He called technicians to his aid and they made him a steel sphere. Zelikoff pumped out the air until there was an absolute vacuum in this artificial sky. Then he filled it with a mixture of gases, imitating the conditions in the atmosphere above the ozone layer (as shown by the rockets). The mixture, which contained oxygen and nitrogen as well as other gases, was then exposed to ultra-violet rays from a strong lamp, which had been placed inside the sphere and played the part of the synthetic sun. Finally he photographed the results inside this artificial sky with a built-in spectral camera.

Zelikoff's experiment was most encouraging. From the bands of colour shown on the photographs he could deduce that the ultra-violet rays of his "sun" had split the oxygen molecules which normally consist of two atoms each. These single atoms of oxygen wandered aimlessly through the atmosphere of the steel sphere. Each one of them carried a small electric charge, imparted to it by the ultra-violet rays, and a few of them reacted directly with the nitrogen, causing a faint glow.

Zelikoff believed that this process also occurred naturally above the ozone layer. He knew that monatomic oxygen reacts easily with other substances, and he now introduced a new compound into his sphere, namely nitric oxide. The results were just as he expected. The single atoms of oxygen combined with the nitric oxide to form nitrogen dioxide, and at the same time released the energy imparted to them by the ultra-violet rays which took the form of light:

$$NO + O = NO_2 + energy$$

Even this result did not satisfy Zelikoff and his colleagues. They wanted to repeat the laboratory experiment under natural conditions; in other words a rocket was to release nitric oxide above the ozone layer. Up there the ultra-violet rays of the sun had split the oxygen molecules during the daytime, and the resulting atoms had combined with the small amounts of nitrogen present, giving off light at the same time. According to Adam Riese this process would become more marked if an appreciable amount of nitric oxide were added, and there were great hopes that a recognisable glow would appear.

The night of the 13th March, 1956, was a clear and star-lit one, typical of New Mexico. The technical staff of the Holloman experimental airfield had been busy all day, and as the hands of the clock moved towards midnight all preparations had been completed. The twenty-three-foot long, slim body of the Aerobee rocket stood on its starting ramp in the beam of several searchlights. Zelikoff had placed two glass vessels, surrounded by wire mesh, in the head. They contained nitric oxide which was to be released into the atmosphere at a height of about sixty miles by a clockwork mechanism, or if that should fail, an alternative radio release was provided.

At exactly one forty-five on the morning of 14th March, 1956, Zelikoff started the rocket from his bunker. While its flight was being followed by a radar screen, other observers on a hill sixty miles away trained their telescopes on the region of the sky where, according to their calculations, the nitric oxide was to be released.

The miracle really took place. Exactly one hundred and fifty-five seconds after the start of the rocket a reddish-yellow light appeared in the sky at a height of sixty miles; a shining cloud of gas half as bright as the full moon and twice as bright as Venus. The first man-made starlight!

For ten minutes it remained in the night sky, clearly visible to the naked eye. It gradually grew in size until it was four times the size of the full moon, getting fainter as it increased, and changing colour from reddish-yellow to silver-grey. After twenty minutes it could only be seen through a telescope, but although very faint by now, it was still there.

Zelikoff watched the light in the sky and once more ran over in his mind the steps leading to it.

1. During the day the ultra-violet rays from the sun had

split the diatomic oxygen molecules into two atoms of oxygen.

2. The nitric oxide molecules combined with atomic oxygen to form nitrogen dioxide (NO_2), at the same time causing a glow in the air.

3. The nitrogen dioxide molecules captured new atoms of oxygen and broke down into nitric oxide (NO) and molecular oxygen (O_2).

4. Then the whole process started all over again.

In Zelikoff's opinion other gases besides nitrogen may play a part in creating the nocturnal glow. However that may be, there are obviously forces at work above the ozone layer which man could utilise.

The Aerobee rocket carried twenty pounds of nitric oxide to a height of sixty miles and produced a clearly visible light. If we could make a machine which captured atomic oxygen and combined it with nitric oxide the energy released could be used for purposes of illumination. Towns and country areas could be lit at night. Crops retarded by bad weather could be advanced by nocturnal illumination. Night-time rescues could be carried out by artificial moonlight. The right type of machinery might even supply the power requirements of future space-stations. The possibilities are at hand.

21

IS OUR CLIMATE CHANGING?

LET US RETURN TO THE WEATHER. What causes its changeability? Is it a pure accident, a simple whim of Nature which affects the middle latitudes in particular; or is it based on logical, natural laws?

The process is not as complicated as it appears at first. About a hundred years ago a scientist, Dove of Berlin, had already realised that the weather can, on the whole, be conceived as a struggle between masses of cold and warm air. Although Dove's theories at first met with a great deal of opposition, they are now recognised by all meteorologists, and form the basis of the "laws of weather fronts," which are the primers of all modern weather forecasters.

The "struggle between air masses" occurs whenever cold and warm air lie side by side or come into direct collision. Warm air is lighter than cold air and can swim on top of it, like oil on water. Therefore it has no reason to penetrate into the colder air below it. Such peaceful conditions occur on either side of the equator. Between the latitudes 35° to the north and south comparatively cool masses of air near the surface of the earth move towards the equator (the trade winds), while the warmer air higher up moves towards the poles (the "anti-trade winds"). On either side of the middle latitudes masses of warm air confront masses of cold air. Both move to occupy the same region and in the effort thrust wedges into each other's territory. It is as if two armies were manœuvring for position on a battlefield. At first nothing happens, but sooner or later skirmishing parties will collide, and units from each side will penetrate into the territory of the other. The originally straight dividing line becomes broken and irregular.

The peculiar thing about these wedge-like penetrations is that they are not carried out straight ahead but along a curve. It is as if one aerial army were trying to encircle part of the opposing one. We will learn the reason for this later on; let us for the moment follow the attacking movements of the cold air. We know that cold air is heavier, and in consequence it will try to displace the warm air in a forward and upward direction. Two things occur. First, the upward movement causes the warm air to expand and cool, because all gases get colder as they expand. Secondly, as it rises the moisture condenses, as it does when it meets a cold window-pane, for cold air cannot hold as much water as warm air. Tiny droplets appear, form into clouds and fall as rain. When the upward movement is particularly violent it sometimes leads to strong electric charges and we get thunderstorms. Meteorologists call these "cold front thunderstorms," because of the advancing cold air which gives rise to them.

The wedge of cold air does not remain stationary. It advances like the slope of a moving hillside, forcing the warm air to give way whether it wants to or not. As we have already mentioned, it moves not simply upwards, but forwards and upwards at the same time. Since it can move faster high above the ground than only just over it, the warm air tends to overtake other masses of cold air which it may meet, and to move over them. Let us assume that it were to meet a new "mountain" of cold air. It would climb the side of this mountain from the back and would be cooled down once more. Clouds would form again, and rain would fall. Meteorologists say a "warm front is passing" and predict the typical rain that such conditions bring (see diagram).

The middle latitudes are the main arena for collisions

A cross-section of two "mountains" of cold air (*left and right*). The cold air displaces the low pressure area of the warm air (*centre*) in the direction of the arrows. The warm air in its turn pushes the "cold air mountain" in front of it. The warm air rising at the fronts forms clouds and causes rain.

between warm and cold air. If we look at the northern hemisphere we see a huge, ice-blue cap, as it were of cold air above the pole. In theory the limiting region or 'polar front' forms a circle round the globe along the sixtieth degree of latitude. South of it is the region of warmer air masses, which flow from west to east. In general the cold air at the edge of the polar front circulates in the opposite direction, from east to west, so that the two march immediately past each other. This theoretical condition in practice never occurs. Advances from either side rapidly change the shape of the front. Frequently four advance parties are sent southward from the polar air mass—you can get an impression of their tremendous size from the drawing on page 163.

The lines of the southward attack are not a mere matter of chance. There are places on the edge of the polar cap where they start most frequently, and these are situated on the eastern side of mountain chains which lie in a north-south direction: the Urals, the east coast of Greenland, the Rocky Mountains in America and the east coast of Asia. These mountain ranges jut out into the circulating polar air like a breakwater into the sea, and deflect a part of it to the south. This creates the hook-shaped wedges of cold polar air which we see on our weather maps, and which often cover long distances in an easterly direction across the earth.

If an advancing mass of cold air from Eastern Greenland has sufficient impetus, it can flood the whole of Germany and reach the Alps. Sometimes it fills the valleys of the Northern Alps from below, as a river fills up a dried lake. Occasionally the cold air even pushes over the Alps and gives rise to the falling winds described on page 99.

The cold polar air may advance at twenty to thirty-five

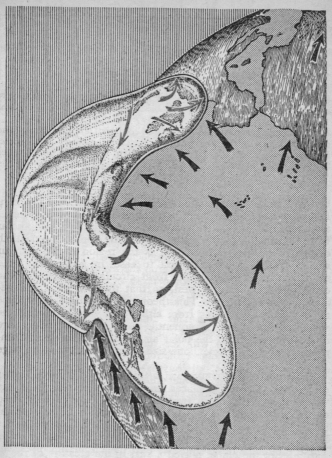

Streams of cold air occasionally flow southwards from the "polar cap" that covers the North Pole. When, in the middle latitudes, they meet warm air moving eastwards they are deflected and begin to move in an easterly direction to form mountains of cold air. Regular "fighting fronts" develop. The arrows on the diagram (which shows a winter condition) indicate the direction of the prevailing winds. The height of the polar air cap has been increased for purposes of clarity.

miles an hour across Asia and reach Southern Iran, where it may still cause considerable damage after a journey of two thousand miles. Advances of cold air in North America can be most dramatic. The air races southwards along the eastern side of the Rockies, as Blizzards or Northers, and frequently reaches Florida. The destructive power of a blizzard is explained by the fact that out of a clear sky the temperature can suddenly drop by 20° C. or more within a single hour. The polar air in Europe does not usually behave quite so fiercely. Before reaching the Continent it has to travel across the Atlantic for quite a long distance and has been warmed a few degrees by the sea water. To the north of the United States on the other hand there are the cold land masses of Canada and Alaska, and there are no mountain chains stretching from west to east to bar the menacing southerly advance of the cold air.

These thrusts of cold air suggest the conditions which must have existed during the Ice Ages, 10,000 to 600,000 years ago. Four cold waves passed across the Northern Hemisphere (with intervening interglacial periods), and temperatures in Central Europe were on the average eight to twelve degrees centigrade lower than those of to-day. Sheets of ice covered the Alps, the Harz Mountains, the Vosges, and parts of Southern England.

The present day flora and fauna of Central Europe could then only live south of the Alps. The causes of the Ice Ages are still not known with any certainty, but it is suspected that variations in solar radiation played a part. Hoyle and Lyttleton are of the opinion that the sun increased in mass due to the addition of inter-stellar dust. This led to an increase in solar radiation and thence to a warmer climate. After passing through the dust clouds the sun grew colder again, and another Ice Age followed. Other scientists believe that a shift of the earth's axis (polar migration), or the exchange of heat between the sea and air in lower and higher latitudes of the globe, played a part in the creation of the Ice Ages.

As we picture the rhythmic advance and retreat of the polar ice cap, we may wonder whether we are living in an interglacial period and can look forward to another Ice Age. It is difficult, perhaps impossible, to give a definite answer at present. There seem to be substantial reasons for believing that we are at the peak of a warm, interglacial age. Statistics show that the ice cover of the Baltic shrank from about 250,-000 square kilometres in 1830 to about 150,000 square kilometres a hundred years later. In his journeys to the North Pole between 1893 and 1896 Nansen found the average thickness of ice to be 3.65 metres, while the Russian Sedow expedition between 1937 and 1940 found the polar ice to be only 2.18 metres thick on an average.

The gradual but constant retreat of many glaciers is another indication that the climate is getting warmer. Since 1870 there has been a continuous withdrawal of glaciers in the Austrian Alps involving twenty to twenty-five per cent of their surface area (in some instances even up to thirty-six per cent). An extreme example is the Muir glacier in Alaska, which retreated thirteen and a half miles between 1902 and 1946.

Two more facts. In the last hundred years the climate of New York has grown so much warmer that one could almost believe the city had moved one hundred and twenty miles southward. During the same time the great salt lake in Utah has lost almost half its store of water.

These examples taken together leave hardly any doubt that the average temperatures in the Northern Hemisphere are actually rising, and the behaviour of plants and animals confirms this conclusion. The tree-limit is moving appreciably northwards. Cereals can now be harvested in regions where before they died of cold. Birds and insects which once bred exclusively in the south now make their homes nearer the pole. Conscientious scientists have recorded that in a certain region icebergs occur less frequently, and fishermen have begun to realise that the cod have been moving northwards year by year since 1917. The amount of cod netted on the banks of Greenland totalled about 350 tons in 1925. By 1951 this had risen to 170,000 tons and in the summer of 1955 even this figure was exceeded. To-day the cod is found to the north of the seventy-third degree of latitude (in other words northward of Upernavik) and already constitutes the main food of the Eskimos in West Greenland.

Do all these facts point to a warm interglacial period that is still approaching? Let us not delude ourselves; the warming up process has only been going on for a few decades, whereas an interglacial age is measured in millennia. It may well be that the gradual warming up is only an insignificant period within a much longer era of gradual cooling. For, as Professor Faust puts it, the consistent temperature change during a few decades is merely a fleeting breath of summer when compared to the immense geological time that constitutes an interglacial age.

There is another interesting suggestion connected with this question. Could it be possible that the warming up of our latitudes is not caused by natural processes at all, but is due to human activity? Could it be connected with the increasing carbon dioxide content of the atmosphere created by industrialisation? Many scientists suspect that carbon dioxide lessens the radiation into outer space, and thus acts as a barrier which retains the warmth created by the sun.

According to the Finnish scientist Keränen, the Arctic thaw stopped some years ago, and the polar region is already growing colder again. The speed of retreat of the alpine glaciers is also held by Italian geologists to have slowed down during the last few years.

This brings us to the theories which contest the gradual warming of our climate as a long-term tendency. Professor Willett, the American meteorologist, a leading exponent of this point of view, believes that the increase of warmth during the last few decades is merely an irregularity in a slow but gradual cooling over a long period. Willett has gone even further than that and dared to predict the climate of the coming decades. In his opinion large areas of the globe will suffer from wet and cold weather. "I warn you," he says, "to lay in a good supply of stove wood and keep your earmuffs handy for the remainder of the twentieth century."

Willett bases his observations on the planetary wind system which is the foundation of our climate, and which is affected by the radiations from the sun and their variations. We already know that such variations are closely connected with sun spots. These spots are occasional irregularities on the surface of the sun, usually occurring in groups of varying number and size. They are visible signs of a "stormy Low" in its flaming atmosphere. The remarkable thing about sun spots is that they do not appear haphazardly, but display a certain regularity in their coming and going. Their rhythm is displayed in an eleven-year cycle during which they become particularly active. Willett's prediction is based on another fact, namely that there is also a longer, eighty-year cycle which is so to speak superimposed on the shorter eleven-year cycle. The properties of the eighty-year cycle are slightly more complicated. For about forty years the sunspot peaks are comparatively low (inactive maxima) but during the next forty years they are comparatively high (active maxima, see graph). Willett elicited these facts by a detailed compilation of statistics back to about 1750.

A comparison of these sunspot periods with the corresponding weather in the United States revealed a curious connection between the two. The periods of inactive maxima coincided approximately with cold and wet weather and those of active maxima with warm and dry weather.

That much was obvious, but at first no reason for it could be discovered. After years of study Professor Willett believed

of emanating rays without first having their nuclei bombarded. They are the radio-active elements, such as radium and uranium. Their radiations consist mainly of three types: alpha, beta and gamma rays. Most artificially made radio-active substances only emit the powerful beta and gamma rays, but very few alpha rays.

There is another independent method of making radioactive substances by nuclear bombardment, and its discovery dates back to 1938. In that year Otto Hahn and his colleagues Lise Meitner and Fritz Strassmann discovered that the atomic nucleus of uranium, not only becomes unstable but comes apart completely when bombarded with neutrons. Each atom of uranium splits into two new elements of lower molecular weight. They fly apart with such energy, and create so much heat when being stopped by the surrounding matter that the splitting of one ounce of uranium 235 [1] has been calculated to give off the same amount of heat as the burning of eighty tons of coal. Nuclear fission also creates radiations. The liberated neutrons penetrate the neighbouring uranium nuclei like bullets. These also split and liberate neutrons in their

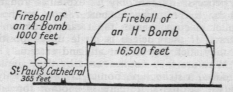

A comparison with St. Paul's Cathedral shows the enormous size of the fireball from an H-Bomb.

turn. A chain reaction is started, which liberates an enormous amount of energy at tremendous speed, the uncurbed course of which is the basic principle of the atomic bomb. The explosion of a normal atomic bomb is caused by the fission of a few pounds of uranium. For a fraction of a second a heat of many million degrees centigrade is generated as well as a strong air-pressure wave and varying amounts of radio-active fission products.

It is the detonation of experimental atomic bombs that is mainly responsible for the radiating substances which pollute the atmosphere to-day. As these materials can create physical and hereditary damage (to which we will return later) their increase is causing serious concern. The amount of

[1] The number behind the element indicates the molecular weight, in other words the sum of the protons and neutrons in the atomic nucleus.

radiating fission products depends on the size and the type of the bomb. There are two main types: the smaller and medium sized ones are called Kiloton bombs, because their activity is measured in thousands of tons of the strongest known explosive, trinitrotoluene (T.N.T.); the larger ones, and the hydrogen bombs in particular (which contain an atomic bomb as a "fuse" to produce the heat required to cause the fusion of hydrogen nuclei), are called Megaton bombs. Their energy is measured in millions of tons of T.N.T. They produce more radio-active substances, unless they are specially constructed "clean" bombs, which liberate fewer radio-active fission products when they are exploded.

There is also a different effect depending on whether bombs are exploded on the ground or high in the air. If a bomb is detonated at a sufficient height, the fire-ball does not touch the earth and the radio-active fission products do not come into contact with the soil. They remain in the air as a fine aerosol (a mixture of air and very fine, suspended particles). If, on the other hand, a bomb is exploded on or below the ground, the fire-ball comes into contact with the earth. Particles of soil are whirled upwards and melted or volatilised by the tremendous heat. Some of the particles come into close contact with the radiating fission products. The heavier ones soon fall back to the ground, where they cause a contaminated area of varying intensity. The lighter particles remain in the air for the time being.

It is known that the heat of the explosion causes an upward draught of hurricane intensity above the site of the detonation. After cooling and condensing this creates the characteristic mushroom of smoke. The rising air current sucks everything upwards at first, like a chimney, and later continues with finer particles and aerosols. The intensity varies according to the type of bomb and weather conditions.

This is the way the radio-active dust reaches the atmosphere. What happens to it then? According to what laws is it borne through the air?

There are two possibilities. A bomb of the Kiloton type rarely lifts the dust particles higher than five to eight miles. This means that the dust remains within the troposphere, the weather zone, where it is caught by rain and air currents. Bombs of the Megaton type blast the dust high into the stratosphere where its behaviour is quite different, as we shall see.

If one investigates the areas where the dust falls back to earth, one can distinguish two clearly differentiated zones. One of them is close to the centre of the explosion and its outer limits are at the most a few hundred miles away from

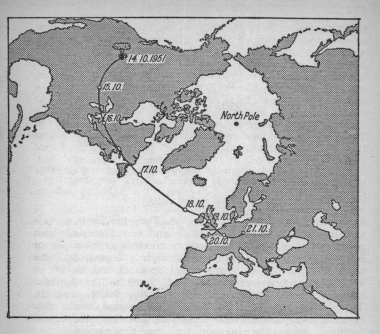

The prevailing winds of our latitudes and occasional jet streams are responsible for carrying radio-active dust from the American Continent to Europe within a few days. This map shows the track of a radio-active cloud which arrived over Germany seven days after an explosion.

it. The radio-active dust sinks back to earth inside this radius within ten to twenty hours after the explosion. This dust is very dangerous because it emits extremely powerful rays. The rays are short-lived, but as the dust has settled so quickly they are still active by the time it returns to earth. The degree of radio-active contamination within this zone largely depends on whether or not the fire-ball has touched the ground. If it has been in contact with the soil the contamination is considerably more persistent. The hydrogen bomb "Ivy," for instance, which was exploded in October 1952, tore a crater two hundred feet deep by sixteen thousand feet wide, and threw many millions of tons of stone, sand and clay into the air.

The second fall out zone lies farther away from the centre of the explosion. Under certain circumstances it can stretch

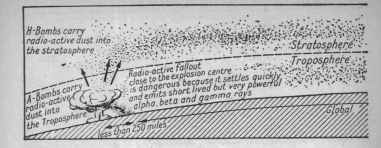

H-Bombs carry radio-active dust into the stratosphere

Stratosphere

Troposphere

Radio-active fallout close to the explosion centre is dangerous because it settles quickly and emits short lived but very powerful alpha, beta and gamma rays

A-Bombs carry radio-active dust into the Troposphere

Global

less than 250 miles

Radio-active dust is produced by atomic explosions and carried high into the atmosphere. It returns to earth over three distinct Zones: *a*. A zone close to the centre of the explosion (local fall out, within 24 hours);

half-way around the world, or even farther. It extends to where the finest radiating dust particles and aerosols come back to the ground after being carried away from the site of the explosion by air currents. They are generally borne earthwards by rain or snow. In the Black Forest, for instance, radio-active rain fell in 1951, 1953 and 1954, caused in each case by atomic experiments in America. Japan suffers from radio-active rain after nearly every major atomic explosion, whether in the Pacific or in Siberia. In many other parts of the globe weakly radio-active rain is no longer altogether a rarity.

The behaviour of radio-active dust which has been lifted upwards for more than fifteen miles by a hydrogen bomb explosion is much more complicated. Up in the stratosphere it is no longer exposed to weather processes and varying atmospheric conditions. The dust is now in a layer of air where there are no vertical movements of any sort, and horizontal movements are almost unknown (if they exist at all). In the stratosphere there is no rain, hail, sleet or snow to grip the particles and carry them downwards. Only the force of gravity remains and very slowly they descend into the weather zone, the heavier ones first, followed by the lighter ones. In the weather zone they sooner or later combine with condensed moisture and are carried back to the earth's surface.

Since only the lightest dust particles are lifted as far as the stratosphere it may be months, or even years, before they sink back to the edge of the troposphere. Therein lies the great danger to mankind. As long as we continue to explode "dirty" atom bombs we will inevitably increase the

Radio-active dust in the stratosphere may take years before reaching the troposphere

Radio-active dust in the troposphere returns to earth within a few weeks in rain, hail or snow

fallout

b. Further away from the centre (intermediate fall out, within one week of the explosion). *c.* A global zone (delayed fall out, the radioactive dust often remaining in the stratosphere for several years).

store of radio-active substances in the larder above our heads. The storeroom over the Northern Hemisphere is even richer than that over the Southern, since the majority of the tests are carried out north of the equator.

It is not much consolation to us if we are told that the radio-active substances possess only a limited activity. Among the fission products of an atomic explosion there are some radio-active materials that are extremely long-lived. The most dangerous of them, radio-active strontium 90, has a half-life period of twenty-eight years. This means that only half the original amount of strontium has been decomposed after it has radiated for that time. The American radiologist Libby estimates that strontium 90 remains within the stratosphere for five to fifteen years. Even in that case it would still fall soon enough to cause damage.

What is it that makes radio-active radiations so dangerous to man? It is simply that they can cause physical and hereditary (genetic) damage. Wherever powerful rays meet living tissue they interfere with the process of life. They interrupt vital biochemical processes inside the cells; they prevent the rebuilding of the cells; they interfere in the activities of the glands and nerves, and they even attack the hereditary factors inside the germ cells.

The physical damage can only be cured to a limited extent. The victims of the two atomic attacks on Japanese cities and the fishermen from the *Lucky Dragon* give terrifying examples of this. A large dose of irradiation causes changes in the blood and varying degrees of skin burns; the spleen and bone marrow in particular are endangered. The rays also cause disturbances of the function of the liver and cancer-like diseases. If the irradiation starts suddenly and exceeds 600 r[2] it causes death within two to four weeks. To cause death more quickly the doses have to be very much larger. Before dying the affected person suffers from nausea, vomiting, hæmorrhage, destruction of the digestive function and thickening of the blood.

Since an unborn child within the womb is particularly sensitive to radio-active rays, exposure of a pregnant woman to a large dose may easily lead to a miscarriage. The birth statistics of the people within a radius of just over a mile who were exposed to 400 or 500 r within a short period during the attack on Hiroshima is a horrifying example. The following passage is a quotation from a pamphlet by Dr. S. Schmidt entitled *Do Atoms Threaten our Health?* "Among the 30,000 new-born babies, there were about 1000 with a degenerate bone structure and abnormal muscular or nervous systems; 429 with malformed organs of smell or hearing; 254 with deformed lips or tongues; 59 with cleft palates; 243 with malformation of internal organs; 47 with undeveloped brains. 25 children were born without brains and 8 without eyes and eye sockets." [3]

These are, however, high doses and the ones we encounter normally and from fallout are infinitesimal and do not produce the severe symptoms of radiation sickness or abnormalities by irradiation of the fœtus.

Professor Langendorff, the radiologist, states that there may be an interval of a few, or even many, years between the start of the irradiation and the appearance of the first signs of damage. Langendorff continues: "There is, for instance, an average latent period of six years for leukæmia (pathological increase of white blood corpuscles) instigated by small doses of rays. Among workers in uranium mines who inhale radon-containing air there is a latent period of about seventeen years from the time they start work until the appearance of cancer of the lung. Women painting phosphorescent figures on watch dials sometimes begin to suffer from bone cancer after twenty to twenty-two years."

In general the rays apparently shorten the human life span. An investigation in America showed that X-ray specialists die on an average five years earlier than doctors who do not use X-rays regularly.

The uncanny thing about the rays emitted by radio-active substances is their invisibility and their ubiquity in the con-

[2] r = Röntgen units. 1 r is the amount of radiation that creates two thousand million pairs of ions in one cubic centimetre of air.
[3] From: Arztliche Sammelblätter, 44th year, Volume 4, January 1955.

taminated area. They can be neither heard nor felt, neither smelled nor seen. In contrast to pathogenic bacteria they cannot be destroyed by drugs. One has to wait until the substance emitting them decomposes by itself. This may take months, years, centuries or even millennia (radium has a half-life period of 1500 years and radio-active carbon of 5000 years).

We have already mentioned that radiating substances can enter the human body in various ways. They can be inhaled, penetrate the skin or be swallowed with our food. Radioactive strontium 90 is especially dangerous. It is related chemically to calcium, the element which plays an important role in the formation of bones, particularly in childhood. If radio-active strontium 90 gets into the body it is preferentially deposited in the bones. It may remain there for a very long time, for the metabolism of bones is extremely slow. It forms a little "machine-gun position" inside the bone whence it continually sends its penetrating spray of "bullets" into the body. Experiments on rats have shown that this causes cancer.

Plants, as well as men and many types of animal, incorporate strontium 90 in their metabolic processes. Thus grass can easily be infected and, through being eaten by cows, can contaminate milk, butter and cheese. In this connection it is interesting to note that strontium 90 comprises about five per cent of all the radio-active fission products. In February 1957 a disturbing article was published in the well-known American journal *Science*. It stated that investigations from seventeen stations, scattered all over the globe, have shown that human bones contained one ten-thousandth of the maximum tolerated dose of strontium 90 in the autumn of 1955. This value would increase to one-thousandth or one five-hundredth by 1970 if the store of strontium in the atmosphere was not replenished. Since the publication there has already been an increase due to the explosion of further hydrogen bombs.

Physical damage only becomes noticeable after a minimum amount of radiation, but hereditary damage can be caused by very small amounts. One single particle can be dangerous if it reaches the right spot, a hereditary factor inside the germ cell. To understand the consequencs of such a "bull's-eye" we must first understand the nature of biological inheritance; in other words, how are the characteristics of the parents transmitted to their children or descendants?

The starting point of our life is the fertilised egg. It contains hereditary factors of the father (from the sperm) and of the mother (from the egg). All the cells of the body, all tissues and organs are developed from the fertilised egg. The whole organism is produced by a process of cell division, in which the inherited factors are constantly reproduced and transferred from one cell to another.

Our inherited factors have a decisive influence. They determine the manner in which we react to our surroundings during the course of our lives, as well as deciding the colour of our eyes, our hair and a thousand other things. When we examine them more closely we find that they are tiny threads of material inside the cells. These threads in the nucleus of the cell are easily stained and are called chromosomes (from the Greek: *Chroma*=colour, and *soma*=body). The chromosomes in turn contain the basic hereditary factors or genes (from the Greek: *genes*=born of, or produced by). The genes look like tiny strings of pearls on very fine threads, and several of these threads twisted together make up one chromosome.

The structure of the chromosomes and their genetic influence can be changed by various means. Such changes, mutations as they are called, are not unusual, for the evolutionary process towards higher, more complex and better adapted forms is based on them. The principle of the survival of the fittest tends to give preference to the reproduction of those individuals who are best adapted to their environment and are most likely to win the fight for survival. This natural selection has been in progress ever since life appeared on the earth, and it has given rise to all the many types of plants and animals that we know to-day.

Very few natural mutations offer any advantages to the organisms they produce. This is quite easy to understand if we consider that natural selection has been at work for millions of years. This long period has given each species the chance to adapt itself very thoroughly to its surroundings. A new and better hereditary adaptation is therefore fairly unlikely. According to the American geneticist Muller, ninety-eight per cent of all mutations are disadvantageous to an individual, if one considers the existing requirements of its environment.

Radio-active rays are one of the causes of mutation, and it does not make any difference whether the rays come from atomic fission products in the air, from cosmic radiation, from X-ray apparatus, from radio-active minerals or from luminous watch dials. The only important point is whether they hit the chromosomes inside the germ cells.

Men have always been subjected to a certain quantity of

such rays. The emanations from certain mineral ores and the cosmic rays are a constant part of our environment, and have played a part in causing mutations ever since the origin of life itself. Natural radio-activity, as well as heat, certain chemicals and ultra-violet rays have provided a degree of genetic change sufficient for the development of all types of living organisms. We have become accustomed to this degree of change in the same way that we have acclimatised ourselves to the rest of our environment, such as temperature and light conditions.

The artificial radio-activity of the air has suddenly increased the amount to which we have become accustomed over millions of years, and this added radiation may prove disastrous to our descendants. The more our germ cells are bombarded with powerful rays the greater is the possibility of hereditary changes, and, as we have already learnt, ninety-eight per cent of all mutations are harmful.

If the new mutation led to the quick extinction of all biologically unsuitable types, the "genetic balance would remain in equilibrium." A considerable increase in radiation, however, would inevitably lead to a larger number of living but abnormal and genetically undesirable people.

This is all the more dangerous because there is already a tendency towards the worsening of genetic conditions. The progress of medicine has enabled mankind to avoid the biologically desirable natural selection. Many people who would otherwise have been doomed to death are alive to-day thanks to antibiotics, insulin, modern surgery, artificial hearts or kidneys and iron lungs. According to the Danish geneticist Westergaard we have created "ecological niches" in which people with hereditary faults can survive and procreate. Although this development cannot be contested from an ethical viewpoint it will, over a long period of time, lead to a deterioration in the genetic inheritance of the whole population.

The maximum dose of irradiation that a man can bear during his life without suffering physical damage is at present estimated to be 0.1 r per week, or 5 r per year. There is, however, no lower limit for the dose which can cause genetic changes (in other words mutations), nor does it matter whether the rays that meet the germ cells are fractions of r over a long period, or stronger doses for a short time. The important factor is the total irradiation a creature receives during the sexually active period (about thirty years in man). The damages caused during this time are inevitably transferred to the offspring, and cannot be prevented or ameliorated in any way.

If a germ cell is hit by a "bull's-eye," mutations can be caused by breaking a chromosome, by interchanging or inverting parts of it or by altering the chemical structure of a gene. The genetic change does not necessarily become apparent in the next generation. Quite frequently a mutant gene is transferred for several generations without becoming evident.

There is no agreement amongst the experts about the natural radiation to which a human being is exposed during the period of sexual potency. An approximate estimate to cover these thirty years is 5 r, but much larger as well as much smaller numbers are also put forward. It is certain that the value is different in various parts of the globe. Cosmic rays are more powerful in mountainous regions because they have to travel through a lesser amount of air, and in the vicinity of uranium deposits the radiation is more intensive than elsewhere.

Since the number of mutations is directly dependent on the irradiation of the germ cells, it is obvious that any increase of the "natural" dose must have deleterious effects on living organisms. Muller believes that a doubling of the present rate of mutation would be catastrophic for the human race, and that an increase of ten per cent would be "just tolerable." He thinks that the dose causing a two-fold increase would be about 80 r. Other scientists give values varying between 3 and 150 r. A realistic figure would probably be between 30 and 80 r over a period of thirty years.

This danger limit can very easily be reached and exceeded, for an X-ray exposure of the intestinal region for ten minutes causes up to 20 r to penetrate four inches into the body. Pilots sitting in front of glowing armatures in modern aeroplanes absorb about 10 r over a course of thirty years from these machines alone. Such examples could be multiplied, but there is a further danger. Radio-active substances are being marketed to an increasing extent. Some are intended for the household: glowing bell-buttons or light-switches, and radio-active toys for children. Television screens also emit a less powerful type of X-ray. Certain radio-active substances are used for purposes of scientific measurement and research and others are used by medical men for ray-treatment.

The danger surrounding us can only be indicated very roughly. Many uses of radio-activity are beneficial and it would be retrogressive and irresponsible to stop them. If on the other hand we do not take sufficient care or do not adequately protect ourselves, we will certainly suffer from genetic defects which we will transmit to our descendants.

Everyone must, therefore, take a serious view of the atomic experiments, which increase the amount of radio-active materials in the atmosphere, for they are the most dangerous source of radiating contamination. It is to be hoped that reason will triumph and that all nations will stop further explosions, and turn their efforts to the peaceful development and exploitation of the energy obtained by the fission of hydrogen nuclei, a method that does not give rise to radiating fission products. The amount of radio-active substances in the atmosphere is already incalculable, and these substances are slowly and relentlessly sinking back to earth. If we do not recognise the danger of increasing this amount, our children and grandchildren will suffer for it.

We must realise the danger before it is too late. "It is an inconceivable event in the history of the earth and of mankind that nature contains radio-active elements which we have created. . . ." Albert Schweitzer declared during an Easter broadcast in 1957: "Thoughtlessly we wander onwards. It must not happen that we will not collect ourselves in time to produce the understanding, sincerity and courage to renounce this madness and to come to grips with reality."

We still have time. Earth's envelope still surrounds us with all its bounty. It curves above us like a protecting hand, invisible but of vital importance to all living things, protects us from deadly space-rays, yielding us life-giving oxygen and regulating the temperature in which we can live. It is within our power to preserve this boon or to destroy it.

ACKNOWLEDGMENTS

For permission to reproduce the illustrations we are grateful to the following:

Bavaria Verlag; Edgerton, Germeshausen and Grier Inc., Karl-Heinz Fell; International News Photo; Kristall; Dr. F. Krügler; Frank W. Lane; Dr. E. Mason; Paul Popper; Press-Foto Seeger; USIS-Photo Unit; Walter Weissenbach. (The illustrations are between pages 96 and 97.)

The diagrams are by H. Pfleiderer and K. Th. Netzer. For the use of the drawings, on which they are based, we are grateful to the following:—

Cross-section of the atmosphere, p. 20-21: after Dreesen (*Kristall*). Polar lights, p. 47: after Gartlein (*National Geographic Magazine*). Tornado, p. 104: after *Life*. Hurricane, p. 110: after *Flying*. Tracks of Hurricanes, p. 114: based on *Fortune*. Jet-stream, p. 118: after Hess (*Orion*). Weather, p. 121: after Ulrich (*Umschau*). Thundercloud, p. 125: after Wolf (*Orion*). Thunder, p. 128: after Webster (*Natural History*). Nitrogen cycle in nature, p. 134: after Kamen (*Scientific American*). Cross-section of an alveolus, p. 138 and 140: after Scherrer (*Kristall*). What are modern aeroplanes capable of?, p. 150: after Hohansson (*Christian Science Monitor*). A. Low, p. 162: after de Rudder (*Meteorobiologie*). Polar Cap, p. 163: after Scherrer (*Kristall*). Sun spots, p. 167: after *Popular Science*. Tracks of Radioactive dust, p. 173: after Radiologische Forschungsstelle University Freiburg (*Press-Foto Seeger*). Radioactive dust, p. 174 and 175: after *Popular Science*.

BIBLIOGRAPHY

ANGELL, R., Mirages—Hot and Cold, Holiday, Aug. 1950

BECHERT, K., Der Wahnsinn des Atomkrieges, Düsseldorf 1956

BECK, F. X., Hagel-Abwehr, Umschau 13/1955

BERG, H., Wetter und Atmosphäre, Wien 1953

BERGMANN, L., Der Ultraschall und seine Anwendungen in Wissenschaft und Technik, 6. Aufl., Stuttgart 1954

BOTLEY, C. M., The Air and its Mysteries, New York/London 1940

BUTENANDT, A., Neuartige Probleme und Ergebnisse der biologischen Chemie (Festvortrag anlässlich der Hauptversammlung der Max-Planck-Gesellschaft 1954)

——Was bedeutet Leban unter dem Gesichtspunkt der biologischen Chemie? Universitas 5/1955

BYERS, H. R., General Meteorology, New York/Toronto

CALVIN, M., Die chemische Evolution und der Ursprung des Lebens, Die Naturwissenschaften 17/1956

CAMPBELL, C. I., Radiostrontium Fallout from continuing nuclear Tests, Science Vol. 124 Nr. 3227

COMMITTEE ON GENETIC EFFECTS OF ATOMIC RADIATION, Genetic Effects of atomic Radiation, Science Vol. 123 pp. 1157–1164

COMMITTEE ON METEOROLOGICAL ASPECTS OF THE EFFECTS OF ATOMIC RADIATION, Meteorological Aspects of Atomic Radiation, Science Vol. 124 Nr. 3212

DIETERICHS, H., Bunte Wolken, Natur und Volk 11–12/1949

DRYDEN, H. L., Fact Finding for Tomorrow's Planes, The National Geographical Magazine Dec. 1953

EISENTRAUT, M., Fliegende Säugetiere, Kosmos 11/1953

EUGSTER, J., Weltraumstrahlung, ihr Verhalten in grossen Höhen und in Erdtiefen, die biologische Wirkung auf Grund neuer Untersuchungsmethoden, Bern und Stuttgart 1955

FAUST, H., Erd- und Marsatmosphäre, Naturwissenschaftliche Rundschau 4/1956

——Die Beurteilung von Witterungs- u. Klimaschwankungen, Universitas 10.5.56

FAUST, H., Die Mannigfaltigkeit der atmosphärischen Fronten, Umschau 8/1953

——Experimentelles zur Wetterempfindlichkeit, Naturwissenschaftliche Rundschau 5/1957

——Klimavorhersage für die nächsten 50 Jahre? Frankfürter Allgemeine Zeitung 13.6.1956

——Organisation und Arbeitsweise des Wetterdienstes, Naturwissenschaftliche Rundschau 11/1955

FICKER, H., Wetter und Wetterentwicklung, Heidelberg 1952

FISCHER, H., Heilwirkung der Atmung, Umschau 3/1955

FISHER, A. C., Aviation Medicine on the Threshold of Space, The National Geographical Magazine Aug. 1955

FOSTER, H., Radar and the Weather, Scientific American July 1953

FURLONG, W. B., Can you trust the Weatherman? Natural History Sept. 1956

GAUL, A., The Complete Book of Space Travel, Cleveland/New York 1956

GERLACH, W., Die Gefährdung des Lebens durch radioaktive Strahlen, Universitas 12/1956

GROEBBELS, F., Vogelflug und Wind, Naturwissenschaftliche Rundschau 12/1956

HABER, F., The Heat Barrier, Scientific American Dec. 1953

HANN-SÜRING, Lehrbuch der Meteorologie, Leipzig 1939

HARTLAUB, G. F., Bewusstsein auf anderen Sternen? München 1951

HERRLIGKOFFER, K. M., Der Mensch in grossen Höhen, Naturwissenschaftliche Rundschau 2/1957

HESS, P., Der 'Jet-Stream,' Orion 3–4/1954

——Numerische Wettervorhersage, Umschau 5–6/1956

HILLABY, J., Fliers describe 'Floating' in Air, The New York Times 22.9.1956

ISRAEL, H., Luftelektrizität und Radioaktivät, Heidelberg 1957

JACOBS, W., Fliegen Schwimmen Schweben, Heidelberg 1938

JAPAN SOCIETY FOR THE PROMOTION OF SCIENCE, Research in the Effects and Influences of the Nuclear Bomb Test Explosions, Vol. I and II, Ueno, Tokyo 1956

JOHANSSON, B. B., How fast is fast? Christian Science Monitor 25.10.1954

KOEGEL, L., Wird das Klima wärmer? Universitas 1.9.1953

KULP, ECKELMANN, SCHULERT, Strontium[90] in Man, Science Vol. 125, Nr. 3241

LANDSBERG, H. E., The Origin of the Atmosphere, Scientific American Aug. 1953

LANE, F. W., Wenn die Elemente wüten, Zürich 1952

LANGE-HESSE, G., Zwischen Erde und Weltraum, Orion 15–16/1956

LAURENCE, W. L., Sun is harnessed to create Food, New York Times 30.12.1954

LIBBY, W. F., Dosages from natural Radioactivity and cosmic Rays, Science Vol. 122 Nr. 3158

LICKINT, F., Grossstandtluft, Tabakrauch und Lungen krebsanstieg, Medizinische Klinik 18/1956

LOEB, L. B., Die Entstehung des Blitzes, Naturwissenschaftliche Rundschau 12/1949

MACHTA, LIST, HUBERT, World-wide Travel of Atomic Debris, Science Vol. 124 Nr. 3220

MAINX, F., Die Gefahren der Erbschädigung durch die Verwertung der Atom-energie, München Medizinische Wochenschrift 19/1956

MANLEY, G., Climatic Fluctuations? A Problem in Geophysics, The Times Science Review, Spring 1955

MARQUARDT, H., Die Wirkung ionisierender Strahlen auf die Erbkonstitution, Umschau 6/1957

MATHER, K., Die Gefahren einer genetischen Spätschädigung durch die Atom-energie, Naturwissenschaftliche Rundschau 6/1955

MEDIZINISCHE KLINIK, Sonderheft über Atomfragen, Strahlenschäden und Strahlenschutz, München 15.2.1957

MILDNER, P., Ein Weg zu Mittel- und Langfristvorhersagen, Umschau 23/1954

MILLER, S. L., A Production of Amino Acids under possible primitive Earth Conditions, Science Vol. 117 Nr. 3046

MORIN, Das Tier als Lehrmeister des Merschen, Natur und Kultur, Oct. 1954

NAUER, H., Wie entsteht ein Kugelblitz? Umschau 3/1956

NAUMANN, E., Probleme des Umweltschutzes bei Kernreaktoren, Ärztliche Wochenschrift 24/1956

NEUWIRTH, R., 'Kerne' in der Luft—eine Voraussetzung für Niederschläge, Umschau 7/1956

——Wetterempfindlichkeit—physikalisch-chemisch gesehen, Angewandte Meteorologie 2/1956 p. 311

NEWELL, H. E., Exploring the Atmosphere, Natural History Jan. 1956

OPARIN, A. J., Die Entstehung des Lebens auf der Erde, Berlin/Leipzig 1949

PAETZOLD, H. K., Das heutige Bild der Stratosphäre, Umschau 17/1956

——Die atmosphärische Ozonschicht und ihre vertikale Verteilung, Umschau 23/1953

RABE, W., Mars: Jetzt der Erde am nächsten, Orion 17–18/1956

RABINOWITCH, E. I., Progress in Photosynthesis, Scientific American Vol. 189 Nr. 5

RODEWALD, M., H. C. Willetts Klima-Prognose, Naturwissenschaftliche Rundschau 4/1956

ROSSI, B., Where do Cosmic Rays come from? Scientific American Sep. 1953

ROTBLAT, J., Biological Hazards of Radiations, The Times Science Revue Autumn 1956

RUDDER, B. DE, Grundriss einer Meteorobiologie des Menschen, Heidelberg 1952

SCHERHAG, R., Wege und Grenzen der Wettervorhersage, Universitas Sept. 1956

SCHIMIDT, R., Flug und Flieger im Pflanzen- und Tierreich, Berlin 1939

SCHMIDT, S., Bedrohen Atome unsere Gesundheit? Düsseldorf 1957

SCHULZE, R., Der Wert der UV-Bestrahlung unserer Kinder und Bergleute, Umschau 5/1956

SCHURZ, J., Der Ursprung des Lebens, Naturwissenschaftliche Rundschau 5/1957

SCHWEITZER, A., Die Atomgefahr, in der wir heute leben, Frankfürter Allegmeine Zeitung 24.4.1957

SHENSTONE, B. S., Flight by Man-Power, The New Scientist 29.11.1956

SIEGMUND, H., Wesen und Ursachen bösartiger Geschwulsterkrankungen, Naturwissenschaftliche Rundschau 9/1955

SLIPHER, E. C., New Light on the changing Face of Mars, The Natural Geographical Magazine Sep. 1955

STÖRMER, C., The Polar Aurora, Oxford 1955

SUCKSDORFF, G. E., Das Polarlicht, Naturwissenschaftliche Rundschau 1/1955

SUPF, P., Buch der deutschen Fluggeschichte, 2 Bde, Leipzig 1935

——Die Eroberung des Luftreichs, Stuttgart 1953

TIRALA, L. G., Heilatmung bei Blutdruck-, Herz und- Kreislaufkrankheiten, Frankfurt 1953

TOEPLER, M., Blitze, Naturwissenschaftliche Rundschau 8/1954

TSUZUKI, M., Erfahrungen über radioaktive Schädigung der japanischen Fischer durch Bikini-Asche, 1955, 31: 988

ULLRICH, K. O., Gefahrenzonen für den Luftverkehr, Umschau 19/1954

UNGEHEUER, H., Mensch und Wetter, Umschau 9/1954

TAUCOULEURS, G. DE, Mars, Scientific American May 1953

——The Return of the Planet Mars, Discovery Aug. 1956

VIRTANEN, D. A., Atmosphärischer Stickstoff als Aufrechterhalter des Lebens auf der Erde, Angewandte Chemie, 65. Jahrg., Nr. 1 pp. 1–11

WACHHOLDER, K., Das Problem der Entstehung des Lebens auf der Erde, Universitas 6/1956

WADDINGTON, C. H., F.R.S., The biological Effects of Bomb Tests, The New Statesman and Nation 8 June 1957

WEBSTER, G., Is there Life on other Worlds? Natural History Dec. 1956

WEICKMANN, H., Können wir es wirklich regnen lassen? Umschau 2/1949

WILLETT, H. C., Cold Weather ahead! The Saturday Evening Post 24 March 1956

WIPPERMANN, F., Bessere Wettervorhersagen mit elektronischen Rechenautomaten, Umschau 16/1956

WOLF, F., Gewitter u. Blitz in der Sicht moderner Forschung, Orion 19–20/54

——Interessante Aufnahme eines Kugelblitzes, Die Naturwissenschaften 18/1956

INDEX

187

Other Books of Special Interest
You Will Enjoy

FRONTIERS OF ASTRONOMY   by Fred Hoyle
An assessment of the remarkable increase in our knowledge of the universe.   (#MD200—50¢)

SATELLITES, ROCKETS AND OUTER SPACE
     by Willy Ley
A completely new book on the development of missiles, man-made moons and the future of space travel, by a noted expert.   (#Ks360—35¢)

LIFE ON OTHER WORLDS (revised and expanded)
     by H. Spencer Jones
A fascinating inquiry into the possible existence of life outside the earth.   (#MD144—50¢)

ON UNDERSTANDING SCIENCE   by James B. Conant
A noted atomic physicist explains the scope of science in our modern world, and gives an historical view of its growth.   (#MD68—50¢)

LIMITATIONS OF SCIENCE   by J. W. N. Sullivan
The boundaries and potentialities of present-day scientific concepts, discussed in layman's language.
     (#MD35—50¢)

NEW HANDBOOK OF THE HEAVENS   by Hubert J. Bernhard, Dorothy A. Bennett and Hugh H. Rice
An illustrated guide to the stars and planets.
     (#MD114—50¢)

MAN: HIS FIRST MILLION YEARS   by Ashley Montagu
A vivid, lively account of the origin of man and the development of his races, cultures, customs, and beliefs.
     (#MD239—50¢)

To Our Readers: We welcome your comments about any Signet or Mentor Book. If your dealer does not have the books you want, you may order them by mail, enclosing the list price plus 5¢ a copy to cover mailing. Send for our free catalog. The New American Library of World Literature, Inc., P. O. Box 2310, Grand Central Station, N. Y. 17, N. Y.

How To Build
A Low-Cost Library

You can build a personal library of the best books for as little as 35 or 50 cents a volume. Choose from thousands of the classics and best sellers in literature, biography, poetry, art, history, religion, reference, and science as listed in a new catalog

Paperbound books in print

If you've often had trouble finding the paperbacks you want—here are over 9,100—with information on how and where to get them. Here you can locate all the low-priced paper books available either by checking the thousands of titles listed alphabetically by author and by title, or by looking under any of the 90 categories where selected titles are grouped under helpful subject classifications.

Order your copy of this unique buying guide today—either from your dealer or direct from RRB, New American Library of World Literature, 501 Madison Avenue, New York 22, New York.

If you order from New American Library please make checks payable to: R. R. Bowker Company. Single copies are $2 net prepaid, or you can subscribe to the four quarterly issues for just $6 a year and automatically be kept up to date on available paperbacks.